Why the moon travels

Oein DeBhairduin

Illustrated by

Leanne McDonagh

Skein Press

2020

A CIP record for this title is available from the British Library.

First published in 2020 by Skein Press

© Oein DeBhairduin 2020

Illustrations © Leanne McDonagh 2020

The right of Oein DeBhairduin to be identified as the author of this work has been asserted by him.

ISBN: 978-1-9164935-0-6

Typesetting and design: Alan Keogh

Printed by L&C Printing Group

Skein Press gratefully acknowledges the financial support it receives from the Arts Council.

www.skeinpress.com

Acknowledgements

Most sincere thanks to Fionnuala Cloke and Gráinne O'Toole of Skein Press. They are eternal optimists who carry within them deep tides of encouragement that have kept this process not only afloat but forward flowing. They adjusted especially well to receiving emails at 2 a.m. with new edits. If patience is saintly, your beds in heaven are well secured.

To my family, especially my father, Owenie, without whom this book would not have been written. Thank you for sharing, caring and gifting me a childhood filled with such beautiful sights.

To the team of Travellers who looked over language use and shared with me new tales and stories from their own lives, I am not only grateful but inspired by your resilience and fortitude.

Lastly to my partner, Dan: *Mo ghrá, mo chrí, mo goixil inix.*

Contents

Introduction

The stories in this collection come from the Irish Traveller community, the Mincéirí, the Pavee, an lucht siúil – different but equally valued names for the community recognised as Ireland's indigenous nomadic people and an ethnic minority.

We are all made of stories. Some are tales we tell ourselves, memories we forever reweave in our minds, about the lives we live; others are from the understanding we have gained from a thousand other tellers of who and what we are and where we have come from. If folklore can be understood as a reflection of the cultural constructs of customs, narratives, beliefs, fears and hopes passed through the community for generations, then the tales that have survived, that have grown, changed and reseeded themselves into our lives, are both strong protectors of our culture and anchors to our living histories.

For a very long time, in our community, we have maintained spiritual activities, connections to nature and the whispering animism in our relationship to the outside world. Travellers have lived on the edges of society and have moved through the ages with feet in two worlds, the modern world and an older Éire, keeping custody of songs, crafts and tales that contain unique understandings of our time and place, which might otherwise be forgotten. Many who speak about us do not know us. What is mostly known are the issues the community faces, such as access to accommodation and educational pathways, barriers to employment, and mental health challenges. While we do experience these challenges to a highly disproportionate degree, they are not us nor the weight of us.

What most do not see is the beauty that burns and beats in the heart of the community, a bonfire of remembrance and connection that blazes high on the hilltops of our collective spaces and strong in the hearths of every home. The hallways and archives of our national institutions – the National Folklore Collection, the National Library and the National Museum – brim with beautiful recordings, research, photographs and manuscripts about us. However, most of this was gathered by settled people rather than by Travellers. This took the recording and presenting of our culture out of our control and denied us the opportunity to contextualise it. The vast majority of what the settled community believe they know about Travellers comes from other settled people and, in light of our history, this needs to be challenged. The importance of the cultural jewels of a marginalised community being reclaimed and retold by its members cannot be overstated.

This collecton of stories is a counterpoint to the commonly held beliefs about us and is a reframing and extending of the cultural conversation to include our voices and our artwork. It was important to me when we started talking about this book that the artwork of Leanne McDonagh, a Traveller artist, be used for the illustrations. This is, as far as we know, the first collection of folktales written by a Traveller about Travellers and illustrated by a Traveller.

As a community we are not short of such tales. However, we have very few spaces in which to share them, so I consulted carefully with family and loved ones when selecting the stories and was careful, too, when writing them to ensure that they were rooted in authentic exchanges and sharings. They are new tellings of old tales. Some are of the ancient world, some of the otherworld, some speak of the dead and others name the living. They record, in part, our reverence for the natual world, the reservoir of knowledge that remains about the animals and flora of our lands, our connection to sacred sites and the understanding that history is not disconnected but is forever revealing itself.

Gammon, our language, is used freely and openly in the stories as this collection is not only for reading, but for sharing out loud, an act that not only helps keep the stories alive but also respects the ancient oral traditions of Travellers. Gammon, also known as Cant or Shelta in academic circles, is one of the most protected and preserved parts of our inheritance, with only a few formal resources to document it. For generations, Gammon was a means of communication between members of the community in unkind or unwelcoming spaces. This use of our beautiful resource has encouraged many to keep it close, but in recent years, we have seen a powerful resurgence in open use, celebration, sharing and reclaiming of this precious but sensitively held gift. Because of this, and the enchanting diversity that arises from utilising a non-standardised language, care was taken in this collection to safeguard the natural variations of use. The words shared have been reviewed by a panel of community members and speakers to ensure that not only are they reflective of a community-based understanding but also that diversity, innate within any language, is honoured.

Traditionally there are three primary aspects to the telling of our tales. First, they are contextualised in the moment and space in which they are shared. Second, they are told as entertainment, which is considered just as important as the life lessons they transmit. Third, they are always presented as truthful and real.

These stories are among the many I carry. They did not come to me fixed in the language of our storytelling; they have lost and gained in many ways. Like all traditional tales they are meant to grow and change with the visions of the teller. They are alive as much as we are alive, they journey as much as we journey and, being among the tales of a nomadic people, they have certainly travelled far. Care has been taken to keep the core points and events in line with the original as far as I can recall.

These stories were recorded around kitchen tables, over cups of tea, stolen hours and bursts of early-morning activity. For Travellers, these tales may be a reminder of the beauty and the ever-present voice of our ancestors and a call to once again share the tales we have inherited. To the wider world, may this book be another crack in the wall that all too often divides us.

May we each live a life worth retelling.

The yew tree

Tharsp sharko

I spent a lot of my childhood in graveyards. Not in a morose way, but in the way that many people from the Traveller community spend time in graveyards. Travellers often don't have a permanent place in life, so when we die, we mark the ground with a stone to show we were there.

We visit for funerals, of course, and the quarter mass. We also visit the graves of loved people on birthdays, on grief days, on high holidays and when the extended family come to town. Every relative, every loved one, every kindred friend is remembered. We go to graveyards to be among those who stand on the edge of our shared experiences, when dreams remind us of them and sweetly sung songs invoke their memories, keeping them alive in stories of how they were and where they exist on the wiry brambles of ancestry.

All those free and able, settled or Traveller, whose hearts were light enough to carry them through the streets of Tuam always went

1

for the quarter mass on 6th June, St Jarlath's feast day. We don't willingly go to sorrowful places with a heavy heart in case the carrying of it would mire us to that place.

There is the old graveyard and the new graveyard and, in the centre, a large space filled with unmarked famine graves. We would gather in the middle, packed tight although the graveyard is huge, as if tied together by invisible strings.

In the west of the old graveyard, there is a grey sandstone memorial cemented into the wall, which is marked with no Traveller's name but it is for Travellers, remembered and forgotten, buried in unmarked graves and unnamed places in the Tuam graveyard and across the world.

Unbaptised and nameless Traveller children were usually buried in unconsecrated ground, in the cradle of ancient sites, lisheens, near holy monuments, blessed wells and other sacred places. On rare occasions, Traveller children could be buried in the consecrated soil of the graveyard, which would otherwise have been barred to them for having neither name nor the grace of baptismal waters. Those who had recently lost a friend, relative or neighbour, could lay their still children at the feet of the deceased. The little baskets would be tenderly carried to their rest in known and trusted arms. In many of the graves of Ireland, at the feet of those who journeyed before us, sleep swaddled children, safe in the care of kind-hearted custodians.

In this graveyard, not far from my family home, stands a scattering of tall yew trees, beaten by age, weather and the waves of grief they have endured from all that pass by them. I recall admiring them as a child, those beautiful solemn figures rooted throughout the sacred space. The high, cold, grey, stone walls and dark iron gates mark the boundary lines between the place of the dead and that of the living.

One year, although we went in June, it felt like an autumn morning, still, clear, crisp and cold, but the warmth of the people brought the reminder of the rising days of summer. I remember asking my father later that day about the yew trees and being told about where they were said to come from and why they are almost always found in graveyards.

Many years ago, on a date not recalled exactly, distant enough to be forgotten but recent enough to still be spoken about, there was a young Mincéir féin, newly married, with a beautiful child and a home filled with so much love and care that dawn brought only joy and twilight no quarrels.

He worked the markets and she spun lace, and the bonny-hearted lackeen left laughter in her footsteps and smiles in her wake. His hands were rough but gentle, accustomed to hard work, and hers, light and nimble, fingertips calloused from the tatting of fine silken lace.

They lived for some years knowing only the glow of shared kindness and hopes of a bright future. One year, however, in the depths of winter, their home was visited by a quick fever and all three were struck by it. Their limbs were heavy and smouldering like the charred branches of the campfire, their laboured breaths like its strangled smoke. By the second day the wife and child had succumbed to it. On the third day, the young man recovered and woke to their loss. His legs were weakened, soft like willow, his pale face awash with sweat like cold winter dew, bleached of charm and warmth. He was bereft and gripped by the loss of his loved ones. His body felt as heavy as dark moist peat trodden on by innumerable feet, gushes of agony deep-knit in his bones struck him when he moved, his once strong being as fragile and jagged as broken eggshells.

After the funeral he stayed by their grave until the night had passed and a fresh dawn was breaking on the horizon. His friends came and brought him home, welcoming him back to the world of the living with company and light conversation, poitín to soothe his heart and good food to rekindle the embers of his wounded spirit.

The next day the man returned to the graveyard until his friends came and, again, brought him home. Each day the pattern repeated. The man would rise from his bed and wander to the graveside, the day would pass and in the stillness of the night his friends would seek him out and bring him home.

Soon he refused to return home, shunning his friends, staying in the graveyard to watch over the grave of his lost ones. He stood, a solitary and bewildered figure, his once bright future in ashes. The man had neither north nor south, nor the track of the road back to who he had been.

Over time his skin became cracked and darkened by the sun, rain and gale. His hair became tangled with twigs, feathers and spiders. As the days passed, he grew colder and fixed, rigid and unmoving. Even his voice, once warm in speech, had changed to a mumble of light creaks and crackles. His clothes withered and grew green with mildew and moss, and his tears, still sharp with loss, were red round droplets against his cracked skin.

His toes, knowing the earth beneath his feet so very well, grew long and twisted, reaching down to the familiar spot and rooting him to the place. His toenails, coiled and gnarled, clawed through the soil and stone, snapping the tangled tendrils in the dank earth beneath the quiet topsoil of the graveyard.

What had once been daily visits, a heartfelt pilgrimage of remembrance and connection, had become the loss of coming home, and he became something else. What stood at the graveside was no longer the shape nor shade of the kind man, the good husband, the doting father, but instead a figure of cracked bark-like skin, green spines from age and red berries from the tears that still spilled from him.

In the lock of his grief the man had become the first ever yew tree.

This tale reminds me that grief can bind us into a rigid loss if we stand in it for too long. If we become unmoving, unexploring of the world and unwanting of the company and kindness of others, we too risk becoming the lonely yew in the graveyard, so lost in our own grief that we lose ourselves.

Why dandelions grow

As beárnan gidge raired

Of all the simple things of my youth, the most vivid is the open welcome of my mother's garden. It stood as a lush green lawn that wrapped around the right side of the kainya. The garden was born at the gate at the front and burst out in defiance of the heavy cement, growing at its own pleasure and will all the way along the side of the home towards the back of the plot.

My mother knew that gardens are not fixed, with plants coming and going, travelling upwards and outwards on new adventures like all things in life. It wasn't just a garden to her; it was a living confidante on harsh days, a listening friend on summer evenings and a delightful distraction when her mind was heavy and buzzed as loud as a beehive. It was held in place by tall walls of that cream pebble-dash so often found in council estates that, with time and the painting of yogurt, hosted a soft green moss and shining cranesbill geraniums in little bursts of hearty purple.

It was a simple garden filled with flowers and bushes that had been gifted to her over the years. Each plant had a tale, a story, an origin and was named after the giver: the white winter rose bush gifted to her by Leo from the market that still carries at least one blossom on Christmas Day, the yew tree from Michael 'Cut-the-Lawn', who lived in a house painted red and blue, the maroon berry bush that grew haphazardly and had begun as a goalpost thrust into the soil for a childhood game.

As children we would be sent out to chase away the little neighbourhood terriers who would wander in and dig in the soil, or sent out with forks and butter-knife blades to cut out the unwelcome growth that seeded itself in the garden of her remembrances.

Of all the unexpected visitors, however, the ones that were always allowed to stay unless picked for a tea or a wort cure, were the golden dandelions. My mother always said that there are three things that men never understand: the sharp edges of a broken heart, the mind of a woman, and the value of the dandelion.

Dandelions were welcomed in my mother's garden as every woman, on one road or another, has endured the trials of the dandelion.

The old ones say that during the great flood, the Mincéirí, in fear, had prayed and willed away the clouds, so there came a great drought when the sun shone ceaselessly and no rain fell, when the skies themselves were emptied and the sun stood fixed in place as their ruler.

At first the skies had resisted the banishing of the clouds, understanding the cycle of the weather and how it has its mark on the passing of each day, but so great was the fear of the great flood that nature herself withdrew the clouds and the rain for the sake of the Mincéirí.

In the beginning, the dry days and crisp nights brought only joy, the warm sweet morning air woke people with a softness and the evenings often saw children playing by streams and ponds. The old would rest under the shade of the hazel trees and songs were the common company of the slow-moving winds.

As time went on, however, people grew weary, dreary, dusty and dry. Animals became ill, plants started to shrivel and even the birds refused the winds, preferring to walk on the earth in search of what food remained.

The drought continued until one day a beautiful young lackeen named Bríd called to the sun in search of an answer. She knew the land. She knew the plants, the trees, the weary rivers and how the fiery sun was slowly quenching the flames of those she loved. But the sun, the sun did not reply.

Bríd turned to climb a steep hill to get closer to the sun so her plea might be heard. Already weakened from thirst and the scorching heat, every step uphill was a struggle that brought with it the whispering urge to surrender and turn back. After a long time, the young lackeen reached the top of the hill.

She again called out to the sun and again the sun did not answer.

Bríd searched the sky and saw a star shining bright in the west and called out to it for counsel.

The star twinkled brightly and, in a voice as gentle as a spring breeze, invited her to follow it so that she might find the answer.

For three weary days she and the star journeyed west. With lungs as dry as kindling and with limbs as heavy as boulders, the young lackeen walked after the star, climbing hedges and hills, pushing her way through brambles and bushes, thin with tiredness and sharp with thirst, until eventually the star stood still.

There, hidden in the corner of the western sky, was the moon.

The young lackeen, excited, called out to it.

Hearing her call, the moon rose and spun in the sky like a newly minted plate of silver.

The young lackeen asked the moon to help bring back the clouds and rainfall.

In reply, the moon reached out and shook the very ocean. Since the coming of the drought, the ocean had been still, still and calm like a well-polished mirror, but now the water began to roll up and down the shore in answer to the moon's awakening. However, like the moon and star, the ocean did not know how to make it rain.

The young girl, distraught, fell to the ground and cried. So great were her wails of loss that the star and the moon looked upon her and wept. The sun, on hearing their cries, finally turned towards Bríd. The young lackeen, in desperation and tiredness, but with a depth of wit and a strength rare in a child of her age, pleaded with the sun to rest. She spoke of life with its relentless presence, of the cracking lands and withering animals, of the river beds that looked like deep, carved scars upon the soil, of red sun-flamed flesh and a world that knew so much disorder. She spoke of the need for rhythm, of the folly of her people who in fear had driven away the natural movement of the sun.

The sun spoke in a booming voice, loud enough to shake the crumpled leaves that remained on the trees and for the cracked soil to give up a thick layer of dust as if the land itself was breathing. The sun explained that it was the people who had banished the clouds, who had implored it to shine without resting, so on it would shine.

Her body exhausted from the trials of her journey and her spirit as brittle as the withered leaves, this last denial was a wound she could not recover from. With a whimper, she fell back against the ground and there the young lackeen died.

The sun looked down on her broken frame and was stirred in a great sorrow for her, for her journey, for her half-lived life, and for her death. It shed tears that fell and mixed with the tears of the star and the moon, who too did mourn for her. Their tears fell to the earth and sank deep into the thirsty soil.

Knowing their part in what had happened, the sun, star and moon gathered in the sky. Each promised the young lackeen that they would never forget her.

Eventually from those fallen tears grew a plant, blessed in the light of the sun, star and moon, and took unto it their shapes and forms.

Among its many names is dandelion.

Even to this day, the dandelion remains embodied with the fiery force of the sun, moon and star and it grants the easy flow of water to those who drink it in a tea. If you look closely at the dandelion, you will see that it resembles the sun when it is in flower, the moon when it is in seed, and the star is in the leaves that grow about its base. If you are lucky and pick it carefully from the ground with a song, you might find that the roots are in the form of the young lackeen.

The birth of the rivers

Risp a skai Iurals

Rivers are places of connection to the older world. They were the sources of cleaning, of cooking, and of quenching thirst. A molly would never be far from either a well or a kind river. My family and those behind us grew up beside the Suleen river and returned to it often. She courses through the green pasture lands of Cloontua in Galway. She goes from being a gentle, trickling stream to a deep, rolling river. The Suleen is not known as a river hungry for the taking of people; anyone who has spent time along her banks would sense that she enjoys good company.

The Suleen is well known to the Travellers of Galway. She features in our songs, in our tales and in the warm memories of many. She was the place of newlyweds, a kind friend to those seeking solace after loss, and, on the eve of St John's day, she was the giver of a blessing to those who would dare to leap off the tall granite boulder that nestles at the turn of the Suleen on its journey to the Clare river.

My summers as a child were often spent on her banks. I'm not sure when I first heard this story or from whose mouth it was spoken, but, when I think of the tale, I think always of the Suleen.

After the great flood came the great drought, and after the great drought came the establishment of fresh waters on the old lands. At first there were only a few rivers in Ireland, and much of the land thirsted for water, hungered for the waves and called out for the flow that would give life and movement to it. The rain had finally returned to the land, but the soil still ached for relief. The people were dusty and the earth itself called out in dry raspy groans at night.

One day a kunia decided to wander the lands as kunic do. He was a short man and stout in build, with smooth, ageless features. His gravelly voice sounded too old for his bright, freckled face. His hair was a bramble of wispy brown that crowned his head like a swallow's nest, and his dark-brown eyes were deep and thoughtful. He had a softness about him, like the freshly grown outer bark on a tree that hides within it the deeper toughness of the old core.

On his travels the kunia came across the first rivers of Ireland, and watched from where and to where they flowed and all the land that was left barren without them. After following the first rivers from rainfall to the ocean's embrace, the kunia decided to build a dam on the widest river he could find in hopes that he could raise the water and divert some of it to the dry lands, the barren lands, the lands of hopeful potential.

At first, the kunia placed stones of various sizes and weights along the river bank. Then he gathered up and dragged heavy boulders into the river to push back against the current and raise the waters.

Soon after starting his endeavour, there burst forth a medill, a shadowy water spirit, from the river's edge. Its body was like the foamy spray of the ocean waves, light but shaded as it moved in the air, like breath caught in a winter breeze, not quite formed yet present, dispersing and condensing, moving in an unseen wind. About its shifting frame were strips of weeds and riverbed growth that smelled of damp soil and a deep decay.

The spirit protested against the work of the kunia. He sought to keep the waters as they were. The spirit knew its current lands, it reigned as lord of the established waves and did not agree to what the kunia was undertaking. The holy man explained his actions, the natural need, the want, the call and, undeterred by the spirit's appearance, continued about his work.

Because the kunia's endeavour was just, the spirit could not actively work against him, so it took to watching him as he built the dam. As it watched, it called out in criticism, mocking the kunia's slowness and his soft-handed placement of the stones and boulders. The spirit questioned whether he had the skill to complete the task of building the dam.

Still, the kunia kept building to raise the waters as high as he could and divert the rivers to barren lands. More often than not, the stones, placed with care but without any great skill, became dislodged and the water poured forcefully through, but he continued his steady pace. His ears paid no attention to the sharp voice of the spirit and his hands laboured on.

Sensing the kunia was not to be stopped by the mocking jibes, the spirit set forth a challenge. It would build a dam, higher, stronger, better than the kunia ever could, and, in doing so, the kunia would have to acknowledge the spirit's superior craft and promise never to have a dam stand in front of him again.

With a wry smile, the kunia agreed and continued to work at a steady pace. Seeing the slowness of the holy man, the spirit raced up and down the lands in such a frenzy that it cut irregular grooves and carved pathways deep into the earth.

The spirit tried to tear the stones from the riversides and the river bed to create its dams, but even the stones knew that the kunia's endeavour was just and made themselves heavy.

The more the land resisted the spirit, the more it dug deep into his task.

Dawn broke and dusk fell, the days came and went, seasons passed, the flowers blossomed and then were taken by the earthy decay. The years rolled on, while both the kunia and the spirit worked away at the dams.

In the end the spirit raised a network of high dams and the kunia raised just one.

The spirit's dams stood tall, strong, firm and impressive and crossed the length and breadth of Ireland. Some of them seemed to touch the sky, while most of the kunia's dam was no higher than the tips of the toes of those who walked by.

The spirit approached the kunia to shame him and boast and bask in the glory of the finished task.

However, the holy man was unwounded by any shame. Instead he delighted in the sight of the spirit's great network of dams and thanked it for its efforts. The spirit, lost in its own triumph, was oblivious to the joy of the holy man.

After a while spent soaking in the sight of the mighty dams, the kunia walked throughout the land, and with a gentle hand and lowly uttered blessing to each part of every dam, he downed the walls, which crumbled at his touch like soft, dry sand. The spirit protested but the kunia reminded him of the oath – the kunia had sworn to never have a dam stand in front of him. The spirit watched in horror, realising it had been tricked, as the newly freed waters rushed forward and filled the spaces it had made in its prideful fever; the deep cuts of its pathways became the rivers, the soft grooves from the dragged boulders became the streams and the lightly trodden spaces between the rolled stones became the running ways of the rain.

From the wit of the kunia and the arrogance of the shadowy water spirit came the many rivers and streams of Ireland.

Where stars come from

Ain bini ludas crush awalt

*Stargazing has brought a deep joy to my heart since my childhood.
It always makes me feel that I am small and inconsequential in
the sheer vastness of the universe and, at the same time, a special
rarity within it.*

*The one thing I wanted for my eleventh birthday was a telescope.
The price of it was beyond the reach of my parents' pockets, but I
wanted it in the way children want something, not quite knowing
how the world works or how far a hard-silver pound coin can
stretch.*

*It was a Saturday morning and with sleep still left in the creases at
the edges of my eyes, I sat at the kitchen table across from the open
back door while my mother leaned against the kitchen sink, cup
in hand, talking to our neighbour, Kak. This was the position she
favoured. It allowed her to look though the hallway to the front
door, usually wide open in welcome, and with a slight turn of her
head, she could also keep an eye on the back yard. While I waited*

for the night to come so I could look at the stars, she spent her days seeing everything.

My father called me from the garden and I found him taping a pair of binoculars to a forked stick. He had found for me the closest thing to a telescope that he could in the local second-hand shop. He twisted the stick left and right while pressing it into the garden soil until it stood in the ground.

I can't quite describe the excitement I felt. A chance to look more closely at the stars! If time could be moved by such a feeling, I would have swept the rest of the day away in that very moment. Instead I had to wait, and wait I did. That night, in the back garden, after dragging out a chair from the kitchen to sit on and with the magic of a homemade telescope, I looked at the crescent of the moon. I was awed by the blurry but bright wonders. My father, with a cup of tea in hand, told me the story of where the stars come from.

There was once a man with a very large family. He was without land or animals but was not short of skills and made his best in labouring, bartering and turning his hand to any request that was made to him. When he worked, his brow would weep with the sweat of his efforts and his limbs would grow tired and tight. Despite this, he worked on.

Although he was a man of high craft with a mind that could adapt to any situation as quick as a flame would take to paper, he was often left without work.

One evening, while knocking from door to door in a village in the heart of Connacht, he was turned away by an elderly woman. She did not need the roof of her cottage thatched, her garden weeded nor the swine in her small paddock culled in preparation for the colder months. However, before he left, sensing his need, she moved to the doorstep and told to him a secret.

'There is a fish who lives in Lough Corrib that once caught will give enough flesh and food that you and yours will never hunger.'

She pointed to the lake in the distance.

The next morning the man rose early from his bed and crafted a hook. He took a simple clothes pin from his wife, bent one half until it resembled the curved neck of a resting swan, and the other half he coiled up tightly like the spiral of a snail's shell and lined it with threads of her hair. He then bound it to a shaft of springy willow and so fashioned for himself a fishing rod. Then he made his way to the lake.

For six nights and seven days he fished, never catching anything. Still he kept casting the line from his boat, feeling the quickening expectation that he would come upon something special.

At dusk on the seventh night, while the man half-slumbered on the coal-toned slats of wood that formed the boat, he was woken by the stirring of the line and quickly rustled himself back into the world. A rising excitement bubbled in him. His tired breath formed little pockets of warmth in front of his face before being snatched away by the sharp, frozen claws of the wind. He slowly drew the hooked fish up to the surface. Each pull wrapped the reclaimed thread more tightly around his bitterly cold fingers, which he curled into his palm for warmth.

Slowly he traced the fish in, releasing some of the thread back into the water now and again, giving the fish more space to flitter against the fishing rod, allowing it to tire itself out. When the line finally felt limp, he knew that the fish was spent, and with a repeated curling of his hand he drew the fish up and out of the water into the hull of the boat.

Within moments of it leaving the water, the fish began to swell like a balloon. It was not filled with air but was solid and weighty as if stuffed with shells, stones and gnarls of driftwood. It grew at such a speed that the

fisherman feared it would break and sink the boat.

So startled was he that he rocked it forward in an attempt to push it back into the lake. As the huge fish tumbled over the edge of the boat back into the waves, its eye, now the size of the fisherman himself, popped out and fell with a thud beside him.

As soon as the fish was again swimming beneath the waves of the lake it began to shrink back to its normal size. Like a balloon with the knot untied, it darted away. The eye, however, kept growing, swelling against the sides of the boat, which creaked as if ready to shatter. The fisherman threw himself into the water and swam with all the speed and strength he could muster. Once he was back onshore, he looked to where his boat once drifted but saw only the eye.

To his horror the eye had not stopped growing and the fisherman began to call out to those who lived about the lake. Those who heard him quickly came and those who did not were soon stirred, as the eye had grown to such a size that the water began to spill out of the lake and into the homes of the villagers.

They thought for a few moments of what to do. Would they push the eye up the nearby hill to a valley beside them? Perhaps not, because if it kept growing it would soon fill the valley and smother their homes.

Would they try to set it alight? Perhaps not, because if it still kept growing, they would have a burning, oozing eye instead of just a monstrous one.

Instead they decided that they would come together, pick up the eye and push it up so far into the chilled night sky that the frostbitten breeze would freeze it.

So they first pulled the eye onto dry land to get a solid footing. Then together they picked it up. Some were strong and tall enough to hold it high with their hands and arms. Others rested it on their shoulders, intending to jump when all together they would throw the eye up into the sky. And so they did, with a single roar and a mighty push and jump, up and up the gigantic fish eye went high into the sky.

Quickly the villagers ran from where they had thrown it in case it fell back down, but it stood there in the sky like a much larger second moon. It was stilled by the cold winds so that it no longer grew.

No sooner had the giant eye found a new home in the sky than the villagers realised that it would block out the sun when it rose and may not allow the clouds to pass by with the rain. They lamented that what little crops they had in the fields would quickly wither.

They went back to their homes and returned with pitchforks, hurls, sliotars, wooden spoons, old shoes with the laces uncurled and the lids of pots and pans.

They threw the lids up and out at the frozen giant eye, chipping the side of it into smaller pieces. They swung the shoes around by their laces and, on catching some speed, cast them off, taking chunks of the frigid eye with them as they landed. The hurls were brought out and with fierce hits, sliotars were shot at the eye, causing cracks and splinters. Finally, spoons were thrust up into the air, to catch the remaining pieces of the frozen, broken eye.

By morning the eye had been cut, cracked, splintered and crushed. All that was left were bright specks of dust that trailed throughout the sky. Since then, each night when the sun rests, we see what remains of the eye of the fish – the stars.

Airmid's voice

Airmid's gresko

It was my grandmother who introduced me to the use of herbs. When I was seven, I was bitten on the heel by a horsefly. It swelled quickly, the skin tight with a tint of green. My mother was fearful as my brother and father were severely allergic to horsefly bites. And so Granny brought over St. Patrick's foot, also known as ribwort. She chopped it and boiled it in water with soda bread and applied the poultice to my foot three times a day for three days. On the third day, my skin had relaxed and all the pain was gone. It was like a miracle to my young mind. The herbs had done their duty and sowed in my mind fresh seeds that in time grew into a lifelong fascination with herbalism.

This wasn't unusual in my circle as my family has kept to the old traditions. But this craft has become a rarity with fewer hands plying the trade. Remembering the qualities of every plant not only connects us with our past but honours the sacrifices of many; we only know a plant to be poisonous because someone has suffered to give us that knowledge. Throughout the ages, Travellers have always had a close relationship with the land and its bounties. The old ones' bare feet greeted the soil with every step. People slept beneath the stars, resting on the caring mantle of a sometimes cruel mistress. Herbs and plants not only helped sustain life but they brought healing, revelation, enchantment and promises of survival.

According to legend, many of the ways of herbs and healing were taught to our people by Airmid, an ancient woman from before time was. According to lore, Airmid was the daughter of Dian Cécht, the best-known and most skilled healer in the land. She was sister to Miach, also a healer and a man highly skilled in metal work.

Dian Cécht and his children, Airmid and Miach were of the Tuath Dé Danann, nomads, associated with the plains of Roscommon and Navan Fort, who followed battles, work and adventure.

In childhood Airmid and Miach had great affection for each other and for their father, who often lightened the load of a heavy day's work with tales of his skills and triumphs on the battlefields of health. One of their favourite stories was the restoration of the hand of Nuada, which he had lost in battle. Nuada had been famed for his prowess and dexterity, and this loss came as a great sorrow. Dian Cécht had summoned up his great skill and forged for Nuada a hand of silver that replaced, as much as it could, the battle-lost limb.

As they grew, both Airmid and Miach followed the path of the healer, listening, watching and learning alongside their father and the other healers of their tribe. Over the years Miach's skill and fame grew until they outshone those of his father. While once he had been kind and caring to his children, with each of Miach's accomplishments, jealousy grew in the heart of Dian Cécht.

His son's fame grew with five great feats of healing: he had sowed on the breast of a woman; he saved the eye and sight of a child; he healed the lameness in a noble horse's leg; he revived the womb of a woman to safely carry a child; and his fifth feat was to replace the silver hand of Nuada with one of flesh and bone.

On hearing that his greatest achievement had been surpassed, the winds of jealousy in Dian Cécht were stirred into a great storm and he could not stand to hear nor know of his son's accomplishments any longer.

Miach was known to rise every morning and go into the woods in search of herbs for balms, washes and poultices. One morning, Dian Cécht followed him, and with the gales of jealousy roaring in his heart and mind, he no longer saw his son, child and apprentice but an enemy. He drew an iron dagger, which had been gifted to him by Airmid. The blade had been sharpened on cold, grey slate and polished to a glaring sheen. In the shade of the woods, Dian Cécht crept up on Miach and drove the blade deep into his son's left shoulder until the tip of the knife cleaved his heart in two. Miach slumped silently, lifeless and without breath, to the green carpet of the forest floor. Dian Cécht dug a shallow grave for his newly fallen enemy, and decided to tell any who would ask that he knew nothing of his son's whereabouts.

Next to where Miach had been slain grew a small and bright holly bush. In the trauma of the murder, nine drops of blood had sprayed on her waxy deep-green leaves. Within a season the blood had become berries and the once soft edges of her leaves had grown to become protective spikes.

For almost a year Airmid grieved and cried for her missing brother, swearing to speak to nobody if she could not speak to Miach. Lost within her grief and wandering voiceless through the boreens of her torturous sorrow, Airmid's heart called out nightly to Miach. One dawn, in the grip of autumn, Miach came to her in a dream. He told her what had happened and where his body lay without rest in its shallow grave and promised her all of his healing gifts.

Airmid, under the cover of nightfall with only a lantern to guide her, went into the woods in search of her brother's unholy grave. The only sound came from her feet treading lightly through the blanket of rusty leaves. She soon came across the once soft holly bush, and seeing the crimson berries and the needle-like thorns, knew at once that it stood as the marker of her father's crime.

Outside the clearing in which the holly bush stood, the trees had shed their leaves like tears for Miach and the very grass was withered brown in the sorrow of his taking. The forest plain beside the holly bush, however, was lush with the vibrant colours and warm, sweet scents of life. Herbs were bursting through the soil, one for each day of the year, marking the outline of his body, a living effigy. Among them was soft green wood sage crowning his head to bring him peaceful dreams in his eternal rest, red clover to loosen his chest, cowslip over his heart to soothe the inflamed skin, purple burdock below for easing the bowels and starwort for fertility; dead nettles, a delicate lilac colour, outlined his legs to ease his muscles, and dusty yellow yarrow grew like boots over his feet.

Knowing her brother's promises and recalling her dream, Airmid began to study the herbs and learn of their healing properties and powers. Still without words and shunning all conversation, she began to challenge her father in fame and glory as a mender of people.

Again, Dian Cécht grew embittered with jealousy. One evening he followed Airmid into the woods to see where she was gathering her herbs. Once he realised it was from Miach's grave, he dropped to his knees in anger and desperation and tore up the herbs, throwing them high into the air so that they would be caught by the winds of his ire and scattered the length and breadth of Ireland. Cursing him with her voice, cracked from years of silence, Airmid, in her wit, threw up her red cloak and caught four of the herbs in it. She grabbed the cloak, bundled it up, and with her precious swaddled herbs, ran deeper into the woods where her father would never lay eyes on her again.

From that day on, Airmid was said to wander the roads and byways of Ireland searching for the lost herbs, and it was there that it was said she met with the Mincéirí and taught them the ways of herb-crafting in her wise, soothing voice.

The four herbs – onion, horseradish, garlic and sugar beet – caught by Airmid's cloak are combined and stewed to make Airmid's gresko. Gresko, meaning 'voice', is thought to come from the Gaelic word 'guth', and Airmid's gresko is said to hold a cure for any sore throat.

Why the moon travels

Ain olomi ludus misler

My father used to stand in the hallway, beneath the amber glow of the light, equal stepping between the bedroom my brother and I shared and that of my older sister. With a cup of tea in hand and maybe a cigarette, he would recount the old stories and lull us off to a deep sleep. He was gifted these stories around campfires in his youth from old and young alike, who filled the evenings with tales in ever-growing retellings. For many Travellers, the gift of a story comes with the responsibility to retell it, for untold stories pass into the forgotten.

One of the reasons we tell this story is that it reminds us that Travellers are part of the world and the world is part of Travellers. When you don't see or hear yourself anywhere else, stories like this become important as an anchor to where and why you live.

This is one of the traditional stories my father once told me at bedtime. It's shorter than most and, although bittersweet, it has always made me smile.

In a time long ago when the earth was young, the moon was a disc set in the sky, silent and still. Sometimes, in whispered rumours, it was said the moon would visit. When it did, it took the form of a beautiful lady. Charming and alluring, stern and strong, she was a light unto herself and was kind to those of the earth. She guided many at night with light she borrowed from the day, making sure that none would ever lose their way as they travelled near or far from home. It is told that during her time on earth she met and fell in love with a Mincéir.

He was short of stature, slender and wispy, without a single distinguishing physical feature that would stay in the minds of those who met him. Nevertheless, people's eyes still fell in warmth on him. While he was neither sun nor star, he had a secret glow, expressed in unspoken words and graceful motions.

One night, on his way back from town where he had spent the day sweeping chimneys, he decided to cut through a field to get home more quickly. Although his steps were hurried, he found his sight captured by the moon. She held his lingering gaze, and sensing the want between them, she descended from the sky, slowly changing from a sphere of light to the glowing outline of a figure. He was terrified and turned to flee, but she started singing a low melody, the words of which he didn't understand but sensed to be kind and welcoming. He turned back to her and saw her for who she was, not just the moon but a beautiful woman.

She was lovely and fair, with skin like fresh snowflakes and hair like the softest silk, light mixed with grey, like clouds passing through the twilight sky. Her eyes were pale blue, soft as falling snow. She was draped in cloths, dark twilight blue with glints of speckled starlight and backlit in soft copper tones.

Their love was wild, warm and daring enough to charm even the stars from the heavens. She swore him to secrecy, though, as mortal men were not meant to have love affairs with those of eternity. For many years she visited earth once a month and met with the Mincéir in the silence and wonder of the night. They would meet by a young river, and the sound of its trickling water echoed the murmurs of their love. Days, months and years went by but age chased him slowly, for time is halted for mortal men in the presence of eternity. While those around him succumbed to the battering of time, the Mincéir grew older at a slower pace.

He hurried through his days, eager for night to fall. He would choose a camp without the shelter of tall trees and wait for a night without clouds, longing for a glimpse of his beloved. He would sleep with the canvas of the loban open so he could gaze up at the sky or down at the moon's reflection in the river.

In time, his want of her consumed him and ate much of his

joy. The once charismatic Mincéir grew boastful and full of pride. One night in the pub, surrounded by friends, he told them of the beautiful lady of the moon, that it was he she had chosen for a lover and companion.

Of course his friends did not believe him, so he decided he would show them. When next the moon came to the river, the Mincéir hid his friends behind a holly bush, allowing them to catch a glimpse of her. The moon, though, in her ageless wisdom, and always knowing when eyes were upon her, understood he had lied and discovered his friends. She was so shocked and bereft at his betrayal that she turned from her lover and his mortal embrace. She went back to the sky and hid herself in the darkness of the great nothing.

The heartbroken Mincéir called to the sky but the moon would not answer. She loved him and knew that he, despite the wrong, loved her, but now that their passion was known, they could not be together.

Since then the moon is no longer settled upon the heavens but creeps out tentatively each night and searches the earth for someone to love her as much as she would love him. Each time she is disappointed and sorrowfully turns her face away. She returns to rest in the solitude of the great nothing, until the sharpness of her grief is again blunted by the deep well of strength that lies within her and again she gazes hopefully upon the earth. Since that night and every night since, the moon herself travels the sky.

Among other things, this story reminds me of the fragility of trust and the innate desire to love in all people.

The old man of the mountain

A kris féin tom glit

For as long as I can remember I have adored visits to the bog. I love the scent of wild thistle and gorse like a blend of coconut and young lilies, the springy peat beneath my feet and the thrilling unveiling of unexpected plants proudly rooted in spaces you would expect to be barren. My ears buzz to the sounds of leaping frogs making their way from ditch to ditch, bounding into new waters in a chorus of spits and splashes, a beautiful song set against the background performance of fluttering blue butterflies.

Despite taking joy in the space, I was never able to bring myself to enjoy working in the bog. I would watch the cutting of the turf by machine or the scraitheog. Then the sods would be lined up on the green grass and after two days we would do the first turning, followed by the second turning and the standing of the sods, their feet tucked into the ground and their tips leaning against each other to keep them upright. Next we watched the weather keenly and, if wet or heavy, we would turn the sods for a third time, a flip so that the wetness would drain out of each cutting. The dry sods would be stacked, boxed, baled and bagged and carried home by wagon, or in better years by tractor. The sods would be open-thrown into the back yard to be reeked. We would have to return to the bog to find the precious kheirans, those small turf gems that burn bright white like sun-cast diamonds and were worth the time raking the ground with short sticks, swishing back and forth through the peat to reveal them.

I couldn't count the prayers that we would send up for heavy, ashen rain clouds to meet us on the battlefield of the turf in hopes of a Saturday off. Despite it all, I still remember warmly the annual slow drive home along the road, following the wagon of sods as it travelled. Our job was to collect the lucky stray sods, which would inevitably throw themselves from the wagon. We would be sure to never pass a single one, gathering them up as we rolled behind them. Sometimes we would park and pick, but mostly we just slowed down, threw the door open and out would come a hand to whisk away the sod and place it softly in a bag on the rear seat.

Lucky sods were more than lucky, you see; they were omens and tellers of the year ahead, a superstition no one openly believed but kept in the way most people keep such portents, on the side of caution. A bag of bad sods meant a bad year, good sods and all would be well. The first of the turf reek to be burned in the homestead fire should be the best of all the sods.

In tougher years my parents would ensure that we turned our hands to the bog lines of other families. We would raise their sods in exchange for some for our own home. One Friday night, during the bedtime stories, my father broke the news to us gently that we would be going to the bog the next morning. This plan was met with quickly rising voices. My father, being the man he is, cut though the clatter, distracting us and easing the moment with a story, this story of a man, a woman, a goat and the forming of a fire.

There was once an old man who lived high up on a mountain. Each morning felt cold and wet and, at its very best, like the bite of a late November evening. He was so old that when he first lived on the mountain, it had been just a small hill no higher than a Shetland pony.

Life was hard, the weather bitter. A thick smothering of clouds clung to the peak, keeping out the light and warmth, and most days were darksome and dim, even when the sun hung high in the sky.

The old man lived in a small wooden shack that creaked and moaned loudly along with the gales that shouted through the many gaps in the roof and the wooden walls. The shack was small and cramped as if it had been beaten into a crack on the mountainside.

Inside there was only a meagre fire over which a blackened and battered skillet pot hung, and beside it a short, stumpy chair, which the old man also slept in. The cupboards were mostly bare except for a few small parcels of food that the old man was able to forage and a single, sorrowful-looking fork. There was neither a carpet on the floor nor a picture on the wall; the interior was just as grim, worn and mournful as the exterior.

Having once been a kind man filled with the light joys of youth and with a mind that eagerly awaited new adventures, with the rolling of the years the old man had grown as hard as the mountain itself. Life in that wild, lonely place had battered his heart.

The old man was often cold and found his garments lacking. At first, he dressed himself with the fallen leaves that the winds would sweep to him and wrapped supple willow branches about him from the struggling saplings that grew along the mountain. He stacked up the white seedy duff of dandelions as a cuff about his neck, bound soft thistledown around his wrists and feet and wove feathers into his jumper. However, as he grew older, colder and more aware of the gnaw, champ and chaw of winter, he began to grow out his bristly beard.

At first it grew to such a length that he was able to throw some over his shoulders while the rest rolled out about his knees. Then it grew long enough that some could rest on his back like a heavy waxen coat while the rest barrelled in front of him like a long and wiry apron.

After some time, it was long enough to keep him snug and warm, but he continued to let it grow, grow and grow, until some of his whiskers were tucked under his arms, around his neck, flung upon his head like the tail of a broom, around his feet like bristly shoes and even stacked up high on his chair like a wild bird's nest.

On it grew until every corner of the shack was stuffed and the very edges of it creaked with the excess. His beard lined the floor, pushed high against the roof and trailed out under the gap of the door. It rolled up and down much of the mountain and, when the thought came to him, the old man would gather up the tips of his beard and stack it high like the summit of another tall mountain behind the shack.

As more years came and went, the only visitors to the shack were the winds, rains, clouds and gloom, until one day the old man heard the rap of knuckles on his door.

Startled, he rose to his feet from his beard-clad chair by the fire and threw the door open wide with a deep roaring huff at the audacity of anyone who would disturb his solitary silence. He was met by a woman called Gidge.

Gidge was tall and rugged, with a clutch of white wispy hair upon her head, piercing eyes like an August sky and a wry crooked smile that hinted at the hidden laughter in her cheeks. Without any welcome from the old man of the mountain, she took quick-paced steps into the shack. Shaking the coldness of her journey from her, she inched towards the meagre fire in the corner.

Before the old man could speak, Gidge told him of her search for a goat that had wandered off from her herd, how she had been searching for the poor creature for three whole days and how its tracks had come up and across the mountain but had not come down again.

She lifted the lid of the old pot that hung upon the fire with the foot of her climbing staff and asked him if he had eaten her goat. The old man shouted that he had taken no goat and that she should shift, move and make her way back down the mountain. Gidge dismissed the sharpness of his reply and told the old man that she trusted his words but she was deeply tired and that the raw bones of her wanted slumber. She would rest by the fire until the next morning.

When the accidental host agreed, Gidge, with both of her hands, took part of the old man's beard and patted it into a pillow so that she could rest. As soon as her limbs had found their space in the weave and tangle of the beard, she was lost to a deep sleep.

The old man, while bemused and bewildered by Gidge's visit, began to ponder how long it had been since he had a visitor and realised that he had forgotten how nice it could be. Before returning to his own chair, he tucked his beard around her and above her and wished her the sweetest of dreams into the unfolding night.

The next morning, the old man was woken by the sound of a door closing and the click of the latch jarred him back to the living world.

Gidge had left to continue her journey.

From the lips of the old man came a deep, loud sigh of relief. As the days ticked forward that sound echoed around the empty shack and became a lingering whisper that reminded him of her absence. Before Gidge's visit the old man had the company of his own solitude but now he simply felt alone.

At night his dreams were filled with glimpses of her, his nostrils caught now and again the light scent of her in parts of his beard, her words remained in his ears and some of his bristles kept the indentation of her sleeping form.

One morning, some weeks after Gidge's visit, the old man woke to the sound of a goat bleating near his door. Immediately he thought of Gidge and her lost goat. He decided he would return the goat to her.

Tying a braided part of his whiskers to the goat as a lead, he inched his way down the mountain. Each step was a great effort as his beard tangled and dragged on every stone, weed, twig and crevice, but still he staggered on in search of Gidge. His search for her led him up and down the country, trailing his mighty beard behind him, much of it becoming so knotted in some of the snares he passed that he would often cut that part away and continue along his journey.

Gidge, however, was not easy to find. He looked to the dry lands of the south, to the valleys of the north, to the great waters of the west and eventually made his way to the land's edge in the east.

He met Gidge on a beach along the eastern shore of Éire, coming upon her as she gathered up crabs and cockles, and she was surprised to see him and her lost goat.

Once she heard of his quest to return the goat to her, she placed a tender kiss on his forehead as a thanks and invited him to sit beside her fire and rest as she had once done by his. He was welcomed to keep company with her for as long as he wished.

That night the old man of the mountain took most of what was left of his beard and made a blanket out of it, on which he and Gidge sat well into the night, talking and whispering of life, under the stars.

The next morning the old man cut off the very last of his beard, knowing that the presence of Gidge was enough warmth to see him through even the harshest of winters.

Since those days, the old man's beard that had been snagged and cut away has become what we now call the boglands. If dug up and set aflame, it will share with you the warmth that was felt between Gidge and the old man.

The women who gather

A beoir thú mala aswuirt

The first story I recall telling was a tale that I had heard at school. I was about nine. I sat on a small wooden chair in the back yard and watched my father and a neighbour cut sods of soil in the garden in an attempt to dig out a foundation for a small shed that was never to be. The groove that was marked that day still exists and each time I see it, I am reminded of the sharing of stories.

The tale I had heard at school was about the Virgin Mary and the Christ child. They hid in a cave from some soldiers and a kind spider weaved a web so thick about the entrance of the cave that the soldiers did not venture in, deciding that no one had passed that way in many a year.

I had only half heard it before deciding to pass it on. I was small, a wisp of a subleen, short on words and shy in company, but the anticipation of having a tale to retell filled my footsteps home with a subtle joy and a loud excitement.

I remember telling the story and feeling proud of it, feeling as tall as if I was standing on the chair rather than sitting on it. My father stood for a short time to listen to me, with his chin resting on top of the hand that lay on the handle of the shovel. His grey eyes regarded me kindly until I finished.

After a while he returned to shovelling the soil aside and told me the tale of where spiders come from and why some still wear the red cord on their wrist.

Once there were old women who would travel the land carrying tightly woven willow baskets to gather the fallen bark of crab apple trees, wilting St John's wort plants and any fresh beetroots that they could find. They plucked the flax that grew brazenly along the roadsides and the wool snared in the thorns of the brambles, hawthorn trees and furze. They dressed mostly in black but the edges of their garments were lined in red, white and yellow. Some of the women had additional stripes on their dresses of different colours, one for each of their children, living or departed. Their long hair was plaited in firm braids, and about their hips small beady pockets embellished with medals, tokens and buttons were tied.

Every evening, they would boil and dye the wool red in a big cast-iron pot that rested on the campfire in the heart of the molly in which they lived. During the night they would continue to spin and weave the cords and render them red for young children. They would sing songs of hope and melodies of joy in a chorus of sweet voices with minds of clear intent, stirring and carding and weaving thoughts and prayers into the cords for the young.

At dusk they would gather, at night they would labour, and as dawn came, they would rest peacefully in their beds.

This is how it was for a very long time.

However, as the years wore on, more and more children were born and welcomed into the world and the old women who gathered began to struggle to keep the pace of their labour. They worked and worked and worked to make the cords of red, the colour of blood, tones of deep fire and iron rust. Despite the struggle, they decided that they would keep weaving cords and would one day weave a cord long enough to encircle the entire world so that no child would be without the care of a loving blessing.

Dawn and dusk, night and day blended into one as the work continued and the old women who gathered forgot to stop to eat and rest.

Over time their fingers, once kissed a soft pink with dye, became darker and darker, some brown from the dust of the ashes, others black with the coal of the well-stocked fire that kept the dyeing pot boiling.

Still the old women who gathered worked on. The molly, once filled with songs and dances of joy, became silent as they focused more and more on their task.

The sweat from their brows began to wash away the red from the cords and they became silken grey gossamer. In time the cords became thinner and delicate as filigree, but at their core they held their strength. Still the old women who gathered worked on.

They grew thin and bony as they neither slumbered nor feasted, and they began to shrink. Some of the old women who gathered worked one or two of their own fingers away, while others kept their gathering baskets tightly strapped to their backs, not bothering to take them off between gathering, dying and weaving the cords.

Their hearts remained warm and the task remained their focus.

In time, the old women grew smaller and smaller, less of this world and more of another, until one day they looked like little more than a bundling of fingers, spinning and weaving, with gathering baskets on their backs, adorned with the stripes and shadings that once belonged to their dresses and beady pockets. They had become the first spiders.

Even now they continue their work, spinning onwards and onwards, across the world.

A sense of protection can be found in many sources. In modern times, many of the Mincéirí still wear and tie the cords. They make the red and white cords of Philomena for protection and to avoid being overlooked, the light blue of St Joseph for healing, and the white silken cords of Mary, the untier of knots.

Bees and giants

Beach an tom gloke

We all find our sense of safety in different ways and cling to it at different times. I was about nine before the veil that hung so tightly about me had fallen away, exposing me to the very real dangers of the wilder world. Before then, I had thought myself, as many young people do, immune to all troubles when under the care of a parent.

I was on the edge of Brownes' field, looking up at the sprawling arms of a horse chestnut tree, when I found the bees' nest like a heap of burned porridge in the crevice between two limbs. I can recall it with such clarity that I could be there again in this very moment. I watched in silence, neck arched, as the bees wandered in and out of the darkened eye-shaped hole that was moulded midway up the nest.

Oblivious to all around me, I rose to watch the bees more closely, reaching forward to touch the wire that was wrapped around the base of the tree. I hadn't noticed that it was barbed. My hand quickly found itself deeply impaled on the sharp iron edge of one of the wires. I reared back in panic, tearing a deep jagged cut on my middle finger, which on release from the wire started to pour with blood and I bellowed in pain.

My father, hearing my cries and seeing the splutter of bright red blood, tugged repeatedly at his collar until it came gradually away in a long drawn-out tear, the seams and threads slowly separating and fraying. He wrapped it around my hand, curling my finger forward in a firm grasp around the fabric. He then scooped me under his right arm and moved at such a pace that the fields and walls between us and home seemed to melt way. Hushing me to stay calm, he said again and again, 'Bright blood is light blood. It's close to the skin. You'll be grand, you'll be grand, you'll be grand . . .'

The next thing I recall is being in the doctor's surgery after they had glued my skin back together. We left promising to come back over the next few days. A small white envelope was tucked into the pocket of my mother's coat in case a visit to the hospital was needed in the meantime.

Almost every hour, hands were pressed firmly against my forehead to check my temperature. The tip of my finger was checked and assessed for its colour. My grandmother had a long list of recommendations for soups, teas and healers. Kak from across the road made her way in, suggesting TV shows to watch and radio stations and pre-recorded songs to listen to, to keep me calm, occupied and open for healing.

After about three days, I had to go back to the doctor so that he could remove the bandage to examine my finger. I was more than a little fearful, having grown comfortable with the gauze. The doctor slowly unwrapped the bandage. About a quarter of the way through the process, the pain was intense enough that I pulled my hand away. My father put his arm around my torso to hold me in a steady comfort, while my mother moved her fingers in small circles through my hair. Then he told me this tale of giants, mountains and bees to distract me.

I felt so minded, protected and cared for by them both, and to this day I remind myself of the tale when unexpected challenges arise.

There were once giants who lived openly in the world. They were tall, beastly creatures at least the size of three men and had shoulders the width of a wagon. They were known for their wide, flat feet with stubbed toes and their thick arms. They had small hands with roundish palms but their fingers were long and curling, bone-like and tipped with sharp talons. They had flat, oblong faces with eyes of a cold, fog-like colour that matched their skin, which was corpse-white. Their ears were large and canine-pointed and the lower lobes rested on their broad shoulders. They carried with them the rancid odour of old animal fats, rotting hay and stale sweat.

They were usually seen in a dishevelled state, with hair that looked like it had been brushed with the roots of a thorn bush, soil, twigs and leaves matted through their tangled locks.

The giants wore clothing made from the hides of the animals they caught and ate. They draped the sheets of leather over themselves, crude holes in the centre for their heads and tied about the waist with ivy vines.

They roamed the lands, feasting on whatever they came across – cattle on the pastures, food in the store rooms of taverns, and the fish that jumped along the streams, but most of all they enjoyed the honeycombs from the nests of bees. They might leave an animal or two in the fields, some fish in the rivers or some food in the tavern larders, but they never left a drop of honey. Not only were the bees' nests crumbled to pieces, the trees in which they had built their homes would be torn apart in the frenzy of the feasting.

The bees were timid, defenceless creatures, spending their days among the beautiful offerings of the woodlands, taking time to share in the nectar of the flowers and to soak in the beauty of every petal visited. They sang together in small, busy voices that moved in a bliss-filled chorus through the woodlands.

Of all the animals that endured the terror of the giants, the bees were the first to gather in rebellion against the destruction of their homes. A call was sent out across the lands of Éire and all the bees that could gathered on the western island of Inis Oírr. Above the home of an elderly wise woman, the bees met to counsel each other on what to do.

First, they decided to go to the giants and ask them to stop eating their winter stores.

And so a delegation of bees was assembled and off they went to speak to all the giants in the land. They went eastward and northward, southward and high into the mountains; then they went low into the valleys and wide into every edge and crevice of Ireland asking for the giants to stop feasting on their homes. After a year they returned to Inis Oírr and gathered again above the home of the wise woman.

Their plea had not been heard.

Second, on reflection, they decided they should go to the giants and beg them to stop eating their food.

And so a new delegation of bees was assembled, and off they went to beg all the giants of the land to stop eating their food. They went to markets and courthouses, to the roads and boreens, to the shorelines and riverways of Ireland begging the giants to stop feasting on their homes. After yet another year they returned to Inis Oírr and gathered again above the home of the wise woman.

Their begging had not been heard.

Third, on review, they decided they would go to the giants and demand that they stop eating their food.

And so a new delegation of bees was assembled, and off they went to demand that all giants of the land stop eating their food. They met giants face to face on battlefields, danced around their homes, sang high and loud to each and every one they met, marked each passage they passed and clung together to increase their hum and voice so that the giants would hear their demand to stop feasting on their homes.

After yet another year they returned to Inis Oírr and gathered again above the home of the wise woman.

Their demands had not been heard.

Most now were tired and took to resting on the roof, window ledges, table and chairs of the wise woman's home, who had long listened to the plans of the bees. She, however, was not as battle-worn as they and suggested to them a new plan.

They should go to the blackthorn trees and snap off their sharp thorns, make their way to the hearth of the blacksmiths and gather up the smoky splinters that fall about the anvil, search the midlands for the spikes of the high-grown teasel plant and then gather again on the island of Inis Oírr. By the time the moon's gaze had turned, they had each collected thorns, splinters and teasel points.

So the bees gathered and discussed their previous plans, how they had asked, begged and demanded that the stores of their food would not be plundered, and how each time the giants ignored them, or at most waved their hands in wide swaying motions to cast the bees away as they carried on feasting on their homes.

The bees gathered, hummed, buzzed and reflected on their challenge, and in the end a single thought was formed. They would go into battle.

And so the bees rose, bringing with them thorns, metal splinters and teasel points, and began attacking the giants. They jabbed at their knees, dug deep into their necks, scraped their chests and sliced at their frowns; they pinned back their ears and darted at their legs. They hummed in such a high swarm about their heads that the giants soon lost any sense of thought and mind.

The giants couldn't endure the rise of the bees and began to try to evade them. Some swam deep into the seas while others climbed high into the mountains, taking refuge on the snow-covered peaks, where bees did not care to spend time. Some stood at the very edge of campfires so the smoke would be a deterrent, but most fled into the caves that were deep under the lands of Ireland.

The determined bees followed those who fled into the caves, the underground warrens and grooves in the earth, jabbing repeatedly at any giant they found. The giants cried out and jumped high, beating at the roofs of the caves, so forming many of the hills and mountains of Ireland.

After yet another year the bees gathered once again above the home of the wise woman on the island of Inis Oírr and reflected on what had happened. The giants had, for the most part, been chased away from the main lands of Ireland and the bees could, for the first time in a long time, build their homestead reserves of honey.

Since that day the giants have stayed on the edges and coastlines and in the caves of Ireland. The thorns, teasels and splinters carried so bravely by the once-timid bees have now become a permanent part of them, a blackened thorn on their tails, not only a reminder of their rising but a testimony to their resilient fighting spirit.

The hedgehog and its coat

A griffin an a gráinneog

*The first time I remember noticing a gráinneog was while myself,
my older siblings, Trina and Darrell, and our father were playing
in a field we call 'the grums'. The grums is a patch of grass two
meadows back from the road that curls about itself to meet the
bridge of Cloontua, which stands beside the lands in which our
ancestors lived.*

*It's a small field filled with pockets of ant hives spread out as
randomly as stars in the night sky. It hosts large clumps of rusty
dock leaves, and nettles line the barbed-wire fences, which hang
on old wooden stumps around the perimeter, broken only by a
short aluminium gate that swings downwards and is tied to a
soft-skinned elder tree.*

*The grums is a speckled lawn that can't be seen by passers-by. It is
filled with so much childhood laughter that if the heart was the
measure of a space it would be bursting at the seams. Among the
birch trees that line one of the fringes of the green, is a solitary*

63

horse chestnut tree on which my father carved our names and dates of birth with a short-blade penknife when we were very young.

That horse chestnut tree, we were told, was a bit of a Traveller too, having come to Ireland from another land, and to this day it still holds our names and the dates of our first breaths into a new world. On blistering summer days, we played in the shelter of its wide leaves and, as the seasons turned, we sometimes took its tall, tapered flowers home and put them in cups and jam jars on the windowsill, like candles for anyone lost.

At first sight, I thought it looked like an upturned nest as it crawled near to where we were sitting eating our sandwiches. Eating in the grums was usually impossible as the field would be crawling with ants, but this evening there were very few.

I watched the gráinneog make its way over some tufts of grass and delighted in seeing it overcome a hard cluster of exposed roots, probably unearthed by our play, that splintered out and thrust themselves up like a fist.

At first we decided to take it in turns to sprinkle some of the corners of the bread in a trail to lure the gráinneog away. However, it sniffed the air, ignored our offerings and continued its curious exploration of us. Having eventually made its way into the middle of our group, it paused and just sat there, watching us, its small head tipped with a black nose and thin whiskers, tilting back and forth as each of us talked, as if it was sharing the company of old friends.

And so there we sat, eating sandwiches with a gráinneog, on a fresh spring day, in a field with a tree that carried our names, making memories.

That day as we walked the Cloontua road home, my father told us of how, in all the country, the gráinneog was probably the kindest and most humble of all the animals as it had once done a great kindness with no expectation of thanks and with no frustration at having been forgotten by most.

Not only has its kindness been largely forgotten but other tales in which it is cast as a thief have been told.

'Oh no,' said my father. 'The only thing that little creature ever stole was a few people back from the hands of death.'

This is a Famine story and the story of a much needed, nearly forgotten kindness.

There was once a creature that lived deep in the woods and sheltered under the arms of ancient oaks, thick ferns and rustling, windswept bushes. It was small and oval-shaped, dusty brown with muddy freckles sprinkled on its soft skin. It would have looked like a swan's egg resting on its side if not for its small darting eyes, its ears that looked like a single coin split in two and placed each side of its head, and its long legs that carried it quickly from one place to another to scavenge for berries and worms.

It was a kindly creature, taking no time to quarrel with its neighbours or find fault with the opinions of others; it was simply happy and at peace with its place in the world. It knew the land and the land knew it, sharing with the creature the rarely seen and secret paths and burrows through the woods, showing it where the best mushrooms grew and where the salmon of the rivers met, where the roots of hazel trees embraced one another and where the council of wrens met each morning to exchange the news of the day.

It knew ways to find food that others didn't, places to store it where others would never look and how to travel, mostly unobserved and unbothered.

One evening, on its daily wander, the creature came upon a Mincéir family who had begun to make their molly in a clearing near the edge of the woods. Curious, the creature stopped in the high grasses where it would not be seen and listened to the family as they unpacked a bundle of their items and built their tents. It looked on as they ringed a trail of stones in a circle, in which they kindled a fire, and then later washed clothes in a shallow but free flowing stream that crept past them.

The creature noticed how painfully thin the family were and how achingly slow their movements were. It saw that the father, who was cutting some wood for the fire with a heavy sweat on his brow, had to stop and lay his axe down for a while between blows. It saw how the mother, who was making a dinner in the battered, flame-worn cast-iron pot above the fire, had only a few small clutchings of herbs to throw in, and how the pot rattled, largely unfilled, when she stirred it. It noticed how the voices of the children were mumbled and rough and their eyes were hollow and weary.

While watching and listening to the family, the creature discovered that a deep hunger had begun to crawl and inch itself across the land, and most of the goodness of the food was already stripped from it by the time the people claimed it from the soil. The family were moving to live closer to the sea so that they could fish and pick at the shoreline, as the disturbance had not affected those waters.

Not wanting the family to starve, the creature set off through the woods towards its home to gather up some life-sustaining food.

It brought them juicy blackberries, ripe elderberries and rich amber-coloured hazelnuts, fresh dock roots and bright-green chickweed. It brought them candy-red crab apples, fresh ram mushrooms, new sorrel and morning-cut wild garlic and everything else that it could bring, and left them in small parcels at the foot of the loban, having only the tip of its mouth to carry them in.

Next morning as the family drew back the heavy canvas of the loban, they caught a glimpse of the creature as it disappeared into the undergrowth and, on stepping out, they discovered the gifts it had left. The family rejoiced and feasted heartily. Feeling much restored from the care of the creature, they took again to their travels, promising never to forget its generosity.

Word quickly moved from the mouths of the family to others who had been affected by great hunger that food was to be found in the woods and that a small fleet-footed animal had fed them while they were near starvation.

People came to the woods in search of help.

At first they arrived in ones and twos, then fours and sixes, and soon it seemed like a whole village had descended upon the woods. There seemed to be more people than trees and still the creature searched in every burrow, ever corner, on every path edge for food for the hungry.

The creature soon began to strain from searching and running. One morning it went into the camp and snapped off several hazel twigs from the besom and placed them in short, tight rows on its back so that when it came across food, it could roll over on it, pinning the food to the tips of the twigs for easy carrying. In that way it could bring more food to the starving people.

In time it began to journey further out beyond the woods, into thicker hedges in which some of the food it was carrying would get snared and lost in the brambles. So it took some more twigs, shorter ones this time, and lined its back again, taking the opportunity to also cover its face and legs, as each morsel of food it could carry might very well save a life.

This continued for many years, but eventually, as the seasons moved forward and nature found her own balance again, the soil began to heal, and the famine that had ravaged the earth withdrew slowly from the lands.

One by one, those affected began to return to their homes, in search of a fresh start.

Since those days, however, the besom bristles and hedge-claimed twigs that the creature carried on its back have become its very own coat. Its once long and sturdy legs, which moved so swiftly in search of food, have been worn down to short stumps and the creature now makes its way through its woody home in a slow, tired and steady manner.

The creature, having moved throughout the woods, byways and crossways in search of food, who fashioned for itself a coat from besom tips, twigs and brambles, to carry as much as it could, now has a new name – the gráinneog, the hedgehog.

Many have forgotten the tale of the creature – the great hunger, the kindness and the sharing of food – but the Mincéir family, they remember.

The three sisters and the crow

Sika siskar a gretin gut

In my youth I never knew we were poor or how hard my parents struggled to keep our home together, to ensure we were clothed well, fed heartily and kept warm by the glow of loving care. What I remember is in stark contrast to what the few surviving photographs of my childhood show: bare floors, the peeling linoleum kitchen tiles, a high birthday feast that was little more than a small round cake, and a wall once scorched by an unexpected fire, still dark with the mark that would not be lifted by scrubbing long after the flames were quenched.

This was not unusual of course for the residents of Tirboy, with most kainyas having only seasonal work. Still today, if the labour force of the community were two hands, only the two thumbs could get work.

It was years before the wider world made its way into my

childhood view and I realised that not everyone counted coins so wearily on the kitchen table, that a stolen bag of coal left for an unguarded moment outside of a shop could bring a parent to floods of tears, and that when you cooked, you made enough food for others along the road. We were beyond rich, though, in all the ways that should matter to a child.

Birthdays mostly brought clothes, but Christmas, Christmas never passed without a parcel under the tree.

One Christmas morning, myself, Trina and Darrell rose early and discovered with loud joy the three presents under the tree in the corner of the living room. Two were wrapped in Christmas paper and the third was covered in the brown paper that was used for our schoolbooks. The wrapping was left in shreds around the room as we took to playing with our new toys and became lost in childhood imagination and excitement.

That year I received a chemistry set, a gift I had written many letters to Santa for. At one stage I had decided to stockpile a bundle of them and throw them into the fire as a way to send them quickly so he would know how serious I was about it. Receiving a large number of letters at once, explaining in the many, many ways how I both wanted, deserved and downright needed a chemistry set would, I assured myself, send a clear message.

This almost caused a chimney fire and handfuls of baking soda were tossed in to smother the flames, accompanied by shouting and running to the garden to check for sparks and red spat dust from the chimney's crown. I was both oblivious to the danger and *very satisfied that the commotion would get the message to Santa even quicker. All going well, I would receive my heart's desire.*

My examination of the chemistry set, with its microscope, jars and vials, was cut short by startling words from my sister, who stood in the hallway, pointing towards the door at the end. 'There's something in the kitchen . . .'

Together we moved slowly forward to discover two cardboard boxes on the kitchen floor that shook and squawked when we approached them. Trina, the bravest of us three, timidly lifted the lid of the box nearest to the door, cautiously craning her neck for a peek at what was inside.

Suddenly the lid of the box sprang open and up popped the head of a crow. It shuffled around, cawing loudly at us, its beak snatching angrily at the edges of the box in fear that we might touch it.

Soon enough our parents appeared and my father told us that he had found the two crows in the snow the night before and he could not leave them behind. He reckoned that both had broken or injured a wing and feared that they would die if left in the coldness of the night.

My mother rolled her eyes at his every word and complained about their pungent odour. She said that we didn't need another animal in the kainya. Her heart was still mourning the loss of Brownie, our small, loyal chestnut mongrel, a few weeks earlier. But she did not have the heart to turn them out either. As in the first Christmas story, we were giving shelter to those in need.

In the weeks that followed, the birds recovered thanks to the intervention of the local vet and the diligence of us children wanting to see our new-found friends reclaim an old life. Along the way my father told us the story of the crows; why some wear hoods and how, when people take care of those about them, they can change the world.

There were once three sisters who lived near Lough Corrib. They passed their time quietly and humbly in a small grey cottage that was tucked low behind the shore and was surrounded by a grove of rowan trees that grew thick and lush, as if trying to hide the sisters away from the world. The stones that made the cottage were of the same rock as the walls that stretched up and down the land.

They were distant from the local people, as unknown to most, the three sisters were gifted with the sight, touch and craft of healing. Fearful of being named witches, their only interaction with their neighbours was during trips to the market in search of an item they could neither make nor grow themselves. While they were held in fond respect, the only visitors they received were the travelling Mincéirí, who called every spring to mend their pots and pans and to share stories. They knew the Mincéirí would not find their gifts a cause for concern or fodder for gossip.

The eldest sister, marked by the sight of healing, could cast her vision into the past to see from where a person's ailments came and into the future to see if they would recover. She was tall and strong, with long brown hair in tight curls that danced as she walked, like autumn leaves caught in a soft breeze. On her ankle she wore a thin leather cord in which were knotted tiny brass bells that tinkled faintly as she moved. She had eyes of hazel with flickers of amber that glimmered gold when she sat by the door of her home spinning fresh yarn.

The second sister, blessed by the touch of healing, could pass her hands over a person in sickness and ease the pain of both the mind and of the body. She was smaller and stouter than the first. She had wild wispy hair the colour of sun-kissed corn that she kept loosely tied with a thick red ribbon in a round bun on the top of her head. Her eyes were deep green, mottled with splashes of grey, the colour of the lough beside which she would spend her evenings reading.

The third sister, tutored in the craft of healing, could blend, brew and boil potions and lotions to knit the body and bones of a person back together. She was the shortest of them all and the lightest in frame. Her wiry hair was sunset red and stood out from her head, tousled as if in a frenzy like the sparks from a flintstone. Her clothing was speckled from paints and inks, splashes and tones from the nights she spent painting and singing the old songs in the kitchen.

For a very long time life was smooth and content in the quiet of their homestead, until one night a deep darkness visited the lough and all of Ireland. It came suddenly and heavily, unexpected and unwelcome, and moved through the lands as a low rolling mist, rising irregularly on its own whim in billows of ashen pearl.

As the mist moved, it brought with it a sadness so deep and sorrowful it turned the leaves of the trees a crumbling brown; seeds rotted in the ground and fish swam deep to the bottom of every lough, stream and river. By morning the birds of the sky had lost their ability to fly, and the animals that grazed on the green or drank from any Irish waters stood thin and weary.

The sisters woke to a chorus from the animals that sat about their front garden, loud and angry at what had happened. Some clawed at the soil and tore up the scattering of flowers that had been planted, others cawed and cawed at the calamity, but most simply stood there, looking blankly forward as if the light of their lives and source of their joy had been snuffed out by the rolling mist.

The first sister gently picked up a crow that stood at the threshold of their home. Its beak had been tapping at the hinge of the door, willing it to open and for help to come.

She rocked the crow gently in her arms, singing prayers and blessings to it until she felt a fresh warmth in the fragile bundle that slumbered against her chest. The second sister washed each of the crow's feathers with the softest of touches, taking care to brush its beak and talons and gently petting the bird with a loving hand to welcome it back to health. The third sister began to grind worms, roots, herbs and nuts, making them into little pellets to feed the bird by hand.

The crow's recovery was slow, but over time its once lame wings began to twitch and flap until it was strong enough to take short gliding flights from the window ledges of the cottage into the open hands of the sisters. Shortly after that, it could sustain flight from the door of the home to the gable end, and within a month the crow had enough vigour to return to the sky.

The sisters also set about ensuring that the other animals were cared for. Every creature imaginable that belonged to the lands of Ireland had come to the home of the three sisters; it had become like an ark during the troubling times.

The home was filled to the brim. There were goats in the hallways, squirrels in the teacups and robins in the cooking pots. Frogs rested in the water of the kitchen sink and otters in the mop buckets. Rabbits made their warrens under beds and beneath chairs. Field mice hid in shoes and butterflies slept behind the framed pictures that hung on the walls of the cottage. Pygmy shrews took up residence in the drawers of the kitchen dresser. Deer stood in the back garden and offered their antlers for drying clothes. Hedgehogs curled up along the skirting boards of the rooms and bats snuggled in coat pockets and hat brims.

The crow had been the first to recover and instead of flying away to the freedom of the skies, it turned its heart to aiding the three sisters and the creatures who had also been touched by the ill mist. It would rise each dawn and go in search of healing herbs with the sisters. It brought back blessed medals and scraps of paper with sacred words inscribed on them, holy water in sea shells, and small pebbles, which it left to warm by the hearth of the home and could be used to massage the muscles of those still suffering ailments.

Of all the creatures that had come to the home of the three sisters, the crow worked the hardest to support the healing of others.

It worked so hard that it forgot to make a nest for itself, so it would sleep at night in the hair of the second sister, the bundle of her locks a soft bed.

As time moved on, with the endeavours of the three sisters and the diligence and hard work of the crow, all the animals returned to health. When the last of the animals stood strong and tall, the creatures all gathered in the garden of the sisters to thank them for their kindness.

To the three sisters they gave the promise of swift aid whenever they called, and to the crow they gave a crown made of meadowsweet, dandelion seeds and the tips of the blossoming yarrow.

Delighted, the crow took flight to show its finery to its

feathered friends, but the crown tumbled to the ground. Seeing the crow's dismay, the creatures borrowed spiderwebs and tied the crown snugly to the crow's head like a hood.

Since that day and all days since, a crow will grow the silver reminder of the crown and hood when it does a kindness to another.

How the badger got her stripes

Ke a broc gred a got'a

The skills to survive in a world that can at times be unkind are among the gifts the older generation passed to myself and my siblings. We were taught to lamp for hares, fish for pike, harvest dusty red dock root, and forage for the sweet, juicy berries on hawthorn and bramble bushes. These were both practical skills and a childhood delight and came of course with responsibilities. It is considered wrong to hunt for meat and not eat it or to pick dock leaves and not use them to soothe a burn. It is not only a waste of the bounty of nature but a waste of a day's efforts.

There were many badgers on the lands around us. When we ventured out, my father would insist that we put thin, round, dry branches into our boots to protect against the badger's bite. If we were to disturb a badger, it might grab at and bite our legs and it would not let go until it heard the sound of a bone snap. The branch in our boots would quickly break, tricking the badger into letting go.

The badger, he said, was among the strongest animals in Ireland, both in physical form and in stubborn nature.

As we walked out one day on a late-evening hunt for a hare for Sunday dinner, I struggled along the way. My body was tired for my bed as we trudged through the sprawling fields and down narrow and ever-wandering boreens. To ease me and perhaps inspire me to stop my loud complaining, my father told me for the first time the story of the badger and how she got her stripes.

There once were woods in the east filled with tall, luscious trees whose branches were as wide as the outstretched arms of ten men. The floor of these woods was thick with berry brambles and hardy bushes, an undergrowth of moss, a maze of ivy and a thick carpet of fallen leaves and pine cones. It was filled with the sweet scent of wild flowers and covered in the trackways of many animals.

Among these animals was the badger, who had a brown and silver fur coat, short stubby legs and strong claws. She had stern black eyes that hinted at a curious mind and always seemed to catch the glare of the noonday sun. Her ears were short like the tips of young ferns and she had a small fluffy tail that moved back and forth as she waddled, as if she was sweeping her tracks away as she walked.

Early one morning, as the sun began to crawl across the horizon, the badger was rambling in the woods and she came across a peculiar and alarming sight. She found a large, round boulder that had rolled down from the steep hill and under it was a beoir, still alive but lost in the pain and shock of the experience. Her eyes were half-lidded, her skin a chalky grey, startling against her coal-black hair.

The badger ran quickly towards the boulder and began to dig beneath it with her sharp claws. The earth was firm and entangled with deep, thick roots. Still, she clawed away at the ground beneath the boulder with hopes of making a slope into which she might roll it, freeing the young beoir.

While she worked, her woody calls rang out through the trees for all and any who would help her.

After a while a smoky-grey heron, on hearing the badger, began to circle the boulder and finally landed next to it. It started to peck at the rock, trying to chip it away and make it easier to move.

The heron soon grew tired and the boulder was not much smaller then when he had started. He gave up his pecking, gave his apologies to the badger and took again to the sky.

Still the badger kept digging and called out again for all and any who would aid her.

Next the long grasses near the bottom of the hill began to twitch and rustle. At first it seemed like the wind, until the grass finally parted and a tall honey-brown deer walked out. The deer turned and placed his back legs against the boulder, hoping to rock it back and forth until it rolled off the young beoir and into the growing hole the badger was digging.

The deer too grew tired and the boulder was little moved from when he had started. He gave up rocking the boulder, gave his apologies to the badger and disappeared back into the high grasses.

Still the badger kept digging and called out again for all and any who would aid her.

In the late evening a large figure was seen at the top of the hill. With the sun's glare behind it, it was not at first easy to tell what it was, but as it drew nearer it became clear that it was a large bull. He approached the boulder and placed his wide horns under it, hoping to flip it off and away from the young beoir.

In time the bull grew tired and the boulder had not moved. The bull gave up trying, gave his apologies to the badger and took again to the high hill until he faded away into the tired late-evening sun.

Still the badger kept digging and night began to crawl slowly towards them.

Once the sun had set, the chill of night began to cling to their breath and seep deep into the bodies and bones of the beoir and the badger. The badger, too, began to consider giving up and returning to her business among the trees.

But she shook the cold from her, and with it her doubts, and kept digging. She stopped only once to gather some elderberries for the young beoir and to wash her fur in the waters of a nearby river so that the droplets might roll off her coat and give the young beoir a lifesaving drink.

Late, late into the night the badger kept digging and finally the boulder began to shift. The hole at this stage was deep, and the badger used what was left of the thick roots to chip away and wedge a space under the boulder, and finally, after a great effort, she chipped, rocked and lifted it off the young beoir until it fell into the hole.

The young beoir was free and she began to regain her senses. Just as a fresh dawn was about to grace the sky, the young beoir was well enough to travel home to her camp.

Before leaving, she clasped the badger's grey head in her trembling hands and blessed her. She petted the badger in thanks, comfort and admiration for what she had done. With each stroke a white stripe appeared.

From that day onward, the badger has always had stripes on her face from where she was touched by the young beoir who had blessed her for her strength, determination and strong will.

The screech of the owl

Ulchabhán l'esko

For Travellers, death is a constant companion who either screams loudly or waits in oppressive silence at the shoulders of many. We pass as all people do, but lately the road through the vale is one we journey at a far greater pace than most of those about us. As I recall this tale, the grim touch of death's thievery has been felt by every family. People are torn from us for many entangled reasons. The withholding of shelter, the denial of care, the daily cuts of discrimination on the mind and the pervading indifference of the settled community to the loss of life, love and people, feeds an insidious pandemic. In recent years, death has brought a new companion – despair, who forces the hand of far too many.

In the hallway of my family home, where the front door turns back onto a wall when fully opened, was a small painting of an owl in flight above a lush green land with a scattering of trees. The painting, while not done by a hand of great skill or framed in any elaborate way, hung in that hallway for many years.

It survived many redecorations and the reshuffling of items in the hallway until my mid-adolescent years, when it disappeared. My mother does not know where it went, or when it went, but fondly remembers it. I recall standing by the doorway, head on the edge of the frame, looking at the brown feathered owl caught permanently in the moment of its flight. I was listening to my father retelling this story, while he sat outside on a paint-splattered wooden chair, catching the light of the warm summer day and greeting the gentle waves of neighbours as they passed by.

The night, they say, was still when the voice was heard, calling through the branches of a juniper tree to those who sat in the circle around a fire kindled with hopes of holding back the hungry hands of winter. It was a midway camp, made hastily on the freshly fallen snow – a rarity, as journeys through the sharp winds of the last season would usually be avoided – but the family were travelling across the plains of Athlone to a funeral. Mothers wore heavy shawls wrapped tightly across their shoulders and clutched firmly beneath their arms. The leather hats of the fathers were made ever stiffer by the lazy wind, which cut through them rather than blowing around them. The children, eyes heavy with the weight of impending sleep, nestled against each other.

From under the sheltering arms of the tree rose an owl, feathers silver like the moon and soft as the first breath of morning wind, its obsidian eyes shimmering in the flickering flames of the fire.

'Death is coming,' screeched the owl, with a voice that echoed through the air. 'Death is coming . . .'

The Mincéirí rose to their feet, fear raised, horror in their steps as they ran away. They fled to the highlands and the lowlands, to the burnt lands and to the altars of the stone church. For a day they shook hands, forgave grudges, held each other tight, lit candles against their own shadows and sang loud of hopes and the glory of life.

That night death did not visit, and the family, relieved, returned to the camp where they gathered again about the flames of the fire, made ever warmer by their replenished bond to each other and life. The stillness of the night was only disturbed by their soft murmurs.

Again the owl came and the owl screeched, 'Death is coming. Death is coming . . .'

As before, the people felt the winter chill kiss their bones and fear dance in their minds, and once again they held each other tight through the night, speaking words of hope, of kindness, of love, but death did not visit.

On the third night, the ruffle of feathers was again heard. The owl rose and screeched, 'Death is coming. Death is coming . . .'

This time the Mincéirí let the words fall on empty ears, neither stirring nor startling at the sound of the owl, but the owl continued screeching into the night, its sound clawing and scratching relentlessly.

The mothers cried out, 'Away with you, owl. We will have no more of you!'

The fathers threw stones and filled the air with shouts of anger. The children chose to look upon the melting snow rather than give their gaze to the unwanted visitor.

Just at the first break of dawn, as the world warmed to a new day, the owl took to the wind and spoke no more to the Mincéirí.

In the days that followed most talked of the owl as a liar and a fool. As the days turned to months, months to years and years to decades, those who had the heart to listen understood the message of the owl, made clear and true by the processions of funerals, the markers of graves and the trails of tears left by the Mincéirí ravaged by loss.

Death is coming, be it in the rising dawn or on the far-off horizon. However, for many, kindness, hope and love can make death's new companion a rarer visitor.

The magpie thief

A bug'in gret'in

In my youth, we had a neighbour who was deeply frightened of storms and their children, thunder and lightning. She would insist that the front and back doors of her home were left ajar to allow the weather to pass through, and that the mirrors in the halls be covered so as not to attract any flickers and strikes, and then she would retire, whatever the hour, to her bed to wait out the commotion. Her fear of it all, which poured out of her as if from an over-filled bucket, was almost infectious.

In our home, however, a storm

was considered a break in the heaviness of the season, a chance to clean out and open up. Fresh air, we'd tell ourselves, would greet us after the skies lit up and shouted. Very often a lightning storm came with the loss of electricity. The beeswax candles and paraffin lamps would be dug out from under the kitchen sink and lit for an evening of sharing and pondering before the dreams of night. We would all gather near the Stanley stove and lamps would be placed on the two windowsills, with a mirror behind each to magnify the light. I can't remember the first time I heard this story, but it was surely in the glow and flicker of candle flames in our kitchen.

Storms were owned by magpies, my father would say, and were a reminder to be kind, to be truthful and, most of all, were a warning not to take advantage of others.

There was once a man who was a swindler. He craved money more than friendship and took more comfort in the clinking of coins in his pocket than in the laughter of good company.

He was tall and strong, with striking features – a broad nose and a chiselled chin, eyes the blue of a clear sky at midday, and hair brown and wiry with speckles of ginger and grey. He was handsome, but it was difficult to say why exactly. His smile had a softness to it and he always moved in an unexpectedly graceful rhythm, as if he was about to break out into a slow-paced waltz. He dressed neatly, too, with the slightest hint of wealth, small ruby cufflinks on his plain but crisply ironed shirt and a lean but well-polished clip in which he held his bank notes.

One day the swindler went to a local fair with three old and tired animals and a plan to sell them off: a brown hen who laid no eggs, a red cow who gave no milk and a white hound who would not hunt.

He set up his stall at the edge of the marketplace, a well-known ploy to be among those first seen by visitors to the fair, but also to allow a quick and unobstructed escape. The market was a busy one and the voices of people chorused in a steady hum of activity and interaction.

Not long after he set up his stand, there came along a woman, raggedly dressed, with wild hair that looked as if it had been pecked at by swallows, and she wore shoes two sizes too large for her feet. She clutched and cradled her stomach as she shuffled through the fair.

She noticed the hen and she told the swindler that she was very hungry and needed a good hen that would lay every day but thought that this one might be too old.

'Not at all!' said the swindler, whose voice was as welcome to the hungry woman as sweet runny honey. 'This is the finest hen that you'll ever see and no finer hen there ever will be!'

The hungry woman deliberated as she shuffled up and down in front of the stall considering her purchase. In the end she bought the hen and went along her way.

Later that day along came a man, whose face carried a brambly beard and whose old and tattered waistcoat was missing several buttons. His hands rested around the hollow of his neck and he spoke in a hot, creaky, wispy voice.

He noticed the red cow and he told the swindler that he was very thirsty and needed a good cow that would give milk every day but thought that this one might be too old.

'Not at all!' said the swindler, whose voice was as welcome to the thirsty man as a pail of fresh cold water. 'This is the finest cow that you'll ever see and no finer cow there ever will be!'

The thirsty man deliberated as he shuffled up and down in front of the stall considering his purchase. In the end he bought the cow and went along his way.

Before the closing of the fair, along came a small thimble of a boy whose eyes were cast towards the ground in every conversation. He startled easily and around him he carried a heavy cloak of loneliness, unseen but deeply felt by those who encountered him.

He noticed the white hound and he told the swindler that he was very lonely and needed a good hound that would hunt with him every day but thought that this one might be too old.

'Not at all!' said the swindler, whose voice was as welcome to the lonely boy as a seat at a table of song and storytelling. 'This is the finest hound that you'll ever see and no finer hound there ever will be!'

The lonely boy deliberated as he shuffled up and down in front of the stall considering his purchase. In the end he bought the hound and went along his way.

The swindler packed up his stall and set about his journey home. Halfway there, the night sky grew angry and a crackle was heard in the air. A storm was setting in.

Soon enough a bitter wind and heavy rain were beating back the swindler as he travelled along his way. His once smooth steps became laboured, as if the winds themselves were taking his grace. His journey became a battle against the fierceness of the mighty gales.

When he was within sight of his home, there was a sudden stillness in the storm and a single blindingly bright bolt of lightning crossed the sky and struck him down.

At first all that could be seen was the tossed earth where the swindler had been, but as the weather calmed and the struck earth came to rest, a crevice in the ground appeared. In that very hole stood a bird of white and black. And so the first magpie was born.

The swindler wore white flashes of the lightning on his night-black wings and a slight shimmer on his feathers when seen up close, like the afterglow of the storm itself.

Since that day, the magpie has travelled the lands of Ireland, not cursed in his form but blessed into that shape to learn from his wrongdoings. He still thirsts, so he nests mostly beside running water, he still hungers, so he is among the first to rise in the morning, and he is still touched by loneliness, so to this day he is considered unlucky when seen alone and must be greeted when seen.

The past actions of the swindler endure. Some magpies are gatherers of shiny things, these days lost rather than stolen, and their nests are said to be among the final places to check when rings, earrings and small trinkets go amiss.

Where the fish get their scales

Key skef bog gocha

Most Saturdays and Sundays involved fishing by the Clare river. Her banks were rarely unaccompanied by one or more of my family members who would sit on a tall, upturned bucket, a kitchen chair brought down on the back of the bike or a bundle of cloth heaped up upon itself.

My heart, however, never took to fishing. I would grimace and squirm at the sight of a fish who was caught. I found it unkind, but I knew that any fish that were not for eating would be offered back to the river. Often I'd go along but spend my time meandering along the upper bank, watching frogs, the growth of herbs or following the tracks of animals. I would stay close enough to remain a part of the wandering whids but not near enough to take part in the fishing. The men would sit or stand and wait, talking in hushed whispers so as not to disturb the fish, especially those from past catches who would be wiser, they thought, to the hook.

Of my two brothers, John and Conaire, it was John who heard the call of fishing the most. The stillness of the wait was kind to him, as was the joy of the catch. He would find people to eat the fish, like old Lawrence, May Sweeney and John Silver. People would gladly take his haul, which he usually had wrapped tight in the crumpled papers of The Tuam Herald *and stuffed down a small rucksack as he biked in and out from the riverside. They would bake, stew or fire-draw the fish and their enjoyment encouraged John to go fishing again the next weekend.*

The river, now filled by the rains and estuaries that flow into her as she strolls to the sea, is said to have been started by the tears of a legendary woman, tears she cried at the death of her children during a great famine. She no longer cries, and it is known that the river is now the passage and pathway of the woman herself, as she carries gifts in her hands and offers up the fish that swim through her hair as she walks to those in search of food. For us the river is alive.

Most likely I first heard this story at the riverside, a kind way of stopping my incessant child's chatter.

Once there were a king and queen who lived on an island off the coast of county Clare. There was high ground on the left side of the island, which sloped downwards, shaded by mottled green trees, adorned with grey and brown stone walls and puckered fields, petering out into the cold moss-glass waters of the Atlantic. At twilight, with the sun resting behind it, the island's silhouette looked like a sinking ship and the little white boats were like passengers fleeing its decks.

The queen of the island was known for her kindness and her welcoming manner. She would invite the people who lived about her to dine at her table, giving little thought to the difference between nobility and peasantry. For her all people were of equal worth and she readily gave away her well-sewn silk dresses to those getting married or her horses – tall strong cobs – to those in need.

The king, however, was not of the same mind. He was known for his relentless hunger for money and he hoarded his gold coins and stacks of gems under his bed. His deep craving for wealth writhed inside him like a fearsome dragon, coiling and uncoiling without rest.

He spoke to others at a cold, dry remove and strained to summon up even a sliver of empathy and understanding. She was for all people and he was only for himself but it had not always been that way.

When they first met, all they knew was joy and happiness. Life was freedom, their adventures as wild as the gusts of the free-roaming gales and their deep expressions of kindness were as common as droplets of falling rain. Love was of far more worth than minted metal coins.

His new bride came with a dowry, however, and that changed everything. She brought a large herd of cattle, several caskets of ale and many heavily laden baskets of gold and silver, which in time started to turn the heart of the king from open giving to the tight-fisted clench of keeping.

The once open doors were locked and bowls that had been heaped high with food for sharing and celebration were cracked, broken and cast to the floor. Even the flowers of the garden began to wilt, knowing not how to blossom in such a cold reign.

The new queen grew more and more distressed at her husband's actions. She decided that marriage was no longer for her, but before she could tell the king, she discovered she was with child. She suspected a harsh reaction to her leaving, that he would take the child, his heir, from her, so she kept the news from her husband.

Late into the bloom of her pregnancy, the queen decided she would take a boat from the shores of the island and sail to the mainland, where she planned to go into hiding from the king among her own people in search of a new life. She gave word to only her most trusted of companions and went to the shore, but saw to her dismay that the boat that was to be her vessel to kinder tides was adrift. The wind had caught the sail of the small boat and carried it off and out of her reach.

A rattling shake of desperation came across her, but not to be turned from her decision, she started to wade into the water.

As soon as the waves were as high as her waist, she paced her breath to the rhythm of the tide, readying herself for the swim.

However, the rising crest of the rippling surge had just started to lick her elbows when her own waters broke and the labours of childbirth began.

As she turned to the shore, her baby was born in the ocean, to the brine of the waters, to the tides of the island. And so the newborn came into the world, daughter of a queen and a child of the waves.

The soldiers of the king arrived to make fresh claim to the fleeing queen as she waded out of the waters, the baby in her arms. With no hesitation, she told them she was merely struck by the whips of labour and had sought the ocean for comfort and would return gladly to her husband.

Following the birth, and feeling that she could not leave, the queen found solace on the island, taking care to share what joys she could with those who lived about her, and she poured her heart, like an uncorked bottle, into her daughter. She named her Skai, meaning *water*, as like the waves of the sea she too might one day be free. Driven to madness by the cold greed of her husband, the queen spent more of each passing day in her room, forgoing all visitors but her daughter, to whom she only spoke kind tales of a life beyond the island.

As she grew, the queen's daughter spent what time she could by the ocean. Every morning as the sun broke on the horizon, she could be seen wandering to the shoreline, her tall and slender figure moving effortlessly along the sands of the beach while her long, black, unbraided hair trailed in the salty air, like soft kelp drying in the breeze.

On reaching the shoreline, she would dig her toes into the sand and wait for the foamy water to wash over her. She would wash in the waves, wring out her hair and sit there in a silent but deep delight. The fish of the ocean, like short pale-skinned eels, would wiggle between her toes and feet, nibbling tenderly and playfully at her nail tips or brushing against her skin as a kind reminder that they recognised her presence.

It was there that Skai, the daughter of the queen, felt most like herself.

When she could not be at the shore, she would stand out in the rain, letting it pour over her. She would soak up the wet, the cold, the dance of water on her skin.

Soon after her eighteenth birthday, the king told Skai of an old man in the south who was also crowned a ruler of land and how he intended to marry her off to him. The unification of their kingdoms would bring him both an ally against any foes and access to increased wealth. He had considered the other king's age and his imminent death, which would leave treasure at his daughter's feet that could then be his. The king's voice rose and chirped in delight as he told his daughter this.

Skai was the daughter of a wilful man, a tyrant of a king, but she was a woman true to herself. She had no desire to be married to someone she did not know, love nor want, for sake of treasure. She set about a plot to escape her father and take her leave of the island as her mother had once dreamed of doing.

She gave word to those she trusted, as her mother had done, and put together a plan to have a boat waiting at the shoreline to bring her across the waves to her freedom. Unlike her mother, she entered the bedchamber of her father as he slept and gathered up the bags of gold and silver coins, jewels and gems, and fled, ginger-footed in the dark, to the place of her escape.

A king without a crown and the money to pay unfaithful soldiers for her recapture would be less trouble to her in her new life. His greed and coldness had grown far beyond himself, and his subjects felt no fondness for him and only followed his commands to ensure they had coins in their pockets and food in the bellies of their loved ones.

When Skai reached the beach, she discovered that the boat,

her key to escape, had been untethered and had drifted from the shoreline, out of her reach. Fate had again struck a heavy blow to the plans of freedom.

On hearing her father's soldiers, who had been alerted, she began to panic and toss the coins and jewels into the water so that her father might still be dethroned.

On their arrival at the shore, some of the soldiers began to laugh at her, but most of them, their eyes heavy with pity for the queen's daughter, told her that the treasure was weighty and would not be carried away by the pull of the waters. They would simply rake it out from the sands and return it to the king. Still the daughter kept throwing the jewels and coins into the ocean, trusting that her waves would mind her.

As soon as the last of the coins had left her hand, the fish that lived about the island and met her each morning swam up and rolled themselves on the sand and jewels, coins and gems. The coins clung to the fishes' once soft flesh and became the first scales – coin-shaped and glimmering in the shades and tones of the gems.

The soldiers stood back from the king's daughter, awed by what they had witnessed. She swam from the shore as her mother had tried to all those years ago. The soldiers watched her with mouths agape as she reached the other shoreline and made her way swiftly into a new world, never looking back.

The newly poor king found himself without authority, but the queen, on hearing of her daughter's escape and with the grip of the king broken, once again left her room and spent time with her people, who remembered her and greeted her with great affection. In time, the coldness of the king was shaken from her; he was dethroned and she reigned. Skai journeyed the roads as freely as water flows through the streams and brooks for the rest of her life.

Since that day and all days since, the fish still carry the jewels and coins of the king on their flesh, not only as a reminder of the costs of greed and the loss that can come with coldness but also that true freedom, friendship and care cannot be bought.

The fox's cry

Ga'l komra lugil

We used to hear them cry on frosty spring evenings and at night when the day was done and the home was heavy with a stillness. Their high-pitched call would ring through each room and echo back on itself like an unwanted stranger. It lingered in the hallways and shadowy corners, harrowing and piercing. You would expect that their cries would become part of the daily fabric of life, noticeable but unremarkable. However, each night that they called, each night that they cried was like a fresh loss sweeping over the home and catching the ears of all those in it.

Foxes, we were taught, are cunning and crafty, mischievous at times but survivors most of all, adapting to their environments and ever-pursuing the fulfilment of their needs. Their night call is sometimes so confusing to those unaccustomed to country life that those visitors wander outside in search of someone in need of help. Due to the swift feet of the foxes, they rarely catch a glimpse of the creatures and the good Samaritans are left bewildered by the eerie calls.

While the lamping and hunting of hares for food remains an intact tradition, the harming of a fox is considered sorrowful. Early one morning, when I was twelve, on my way to school with my father, we found a tiny brown bundle on the bend of the road to Gilmartin. At first glance, I thought it was a nest that had been caught by the winds and tossed to the road.

Instead, it was a young cub, curled up and lifeless, a small figure, alone as life went on around her. My father returned home to get a shovel and asked me to wait with her. While I waited, I was struck by how the world moved obliviously about her, people on their morning journeys neither looking nor knowing of her life and its passing. I could see my breath rise and disperse in the silvery autumn air as I stood with her. The warmth of my breath seemed to mock the cold stiffness of this lost precious creature. My father soon returned and laid her to rest beside a bright yellow hydrant on the side of the road. It's since been painted silver, but every time I pass, I reflect that it stands in memory like her headstone.

As we continued our journey, shaking off the unexpected shroud of
loss, my father shared with me the tale of how the fox got its voice.

There once was a woman in east Mayo who was on the cusp of motherhood and had, along with her husband and two other families, taken to camp by a stream on the edge of town. Each family had two lobans made from bent sally rods and covered in heavy black canvas, one to sleep in and one to live in. It was the evening before a large festival and the other women had taken foot to the market square to sell what they could from their crafting baskets, and the men of the camp, knowing the next day would be a long working one, had either retired to their beds or gone into town to seek out work for the new day.

The woman, who people called Gidge, was tending to a fire over which sat a bubbling broth. Her rusty-red hair was plaited over one of her strong shoulders, the braid long enough to touch her swollen belly. She was warmly dressed in loose but well-buttoned garments, and on her feet, she wore a pair of snug-fitting leather boots. She noticed that the flames were getting low. The fuel had been used up by a day of fire-keeping and, with so many away from the camp, had not been replenished. She decided to search for logs and twigs to stoke the flames.

She followed the stream to a curve in the riverbank where tall trees stood and started to pick up the fallen branches that were light enough to carry and dry enough to fuel the campfire's flames. Knowing that a thick grove of trees often shelters a blanket of fallen branches and drying leaves, she wandered deeper to find more dry kindling.

So intent was she on gathering the fuel that she unwittingly wandered deep into the woodland. As soon as she turned her foot to return home, the first pangs of labour came on her. Crippled by the pain, she found herself unable to make the journey back to the molly. For a while she stood with both hands pressed firmly against the moss-covered bark of a tall oak tree. Her back arched as each surge of pain roared through her, each exhale billowing out like the quick-rising smoke of a freshly lit fire. In her fright and panic, she called out for help.

The dense trees muffled Gidge's calls and she was too far from the camp for her kin to hear her anyway. She was only heard by a nearby vixen who timidly approached her. The fox looked at Gidge in confusion and their eyes met. Without words, the vixen understood the pleas of the woman. She jumped up and, with a brush of her tail, stole away Gidge's voice.

Quickly the fox ran to the camp for aid and action. She cried out a single call in the voice of the woman, deep and primal, fierce and echoing. On seeing and hearing the fox, those who remained at the camp chased it away, thinking it an odd creature and not to be trusted.

The fox, fleet of foot, ran back to Gidge, who she found sitting on the mossy blanket of the forest floor, pale and with a cold sweat heavy on her brow.

The fox returned to the camp and this time called to those who were sleeping and roused them from their slumber. They, too, found the sound of the fox strange and chased it away.

Again the fox returned, and this time stood with rigid legs at the edge of the camp and cried out to those who had gone to town, calling down the winding dusty road that led from the camp to the market square. With the day not yet at its end, no one was returning home to hear the fox.

Not knowing what to do, the fox went back again to the woman and recognised that where she once stood on the cusp of motherhood, she now stood on the edge of passing. With her weakening breaths and last labours, she brought a child into the world. After a moment that felt like seven years, the bini gawlya squalled loudly into the woods. Her call shook the very branches of the trees that recognised her new beginning. The woman, whose limbs shook sore with the effort, gently wrapped the baby in her shawl and with the final light of her eyes she bound her voice to the fox.

Nimbly the fox took the girl child, so hastily but lovingly wrapped, back to the camp and was met by the rising voices of those in it, voices tinged with horror when they realised that Gidge was not to be seen.

From that day forward the fox carries the deep call of the woman as a reminder that we have a duty to keep watch over those who, despite their strength, may unexpectedly find themselves in difficult spaces, and to listen to requests even when they come from unexpected quarters.

The good horse

A burradh currie

I grew up with horses all around me, in the dry, rusty dock field behind our kainya, in the golden wheat fields that were edged white with wild yarrow in front, in the low fields to the right and the rising ground to the left. It was not uncommon to wake in the morning and find a mare happily eating her way through the hedging that curved around the garden in front of my childhood home.

Horses were often trotted up and down the laneways, ridden out when the weather was good and fine, and fed by hand with care. On the nights when the weather was rough and as sharp as freshly broken porcelain, when the shelter of small huts and the heavy arms of the crab apple trees offered less protection, they would be wrapped in light blankets and held in regular watch.

I carry with me, however, a lingering fear of horses, which seems to amuse most people. They are powerful, majestic, muni and proud creatures, with spirits, I am told, as soft as daisy petals and wills as strong as the rocks of riverbeds. I cannot remember a time when the cords of fear did not wrap themselves around my breath as I cut through Brownes' field to the local shops.

Most of the horses were cobs, stout, with thick, heavy legs like the trunks of oak trees, shoulders broader and stronger than any man's and with tails that danced from side to side as they walked or stood. They had eyes as dark as night and long teeth, and their narrow faces were striped with pale markings. Their coats were splashes of coal and brown and the tips of the hooves white, like they were wearing stockings.

Although they remain my frightening beauties, here follows a tale of a burradh currie.

They say in the deep dig of night, when the air is still and the moon stands like a silver blade upon the sky, that a heavy hush can fall down upon the land as the trodden roads between what is here and what is the hereafter become hazy and less understood. The spaces of the wild and the spaces inside us, those thinly woven webs of our understanding, can become lax, and the strings with which we tie ourselves to reality can loosen. These are the moments when the world shows us sights unexpected.

The Cóiste Bodhar passes along the highways and byways of the land, seeking out the lost souls of those who would dare to walk the roads at night. It is guided by a shaded figure who bears many but no true mortal names and answers solely to the gasps of death. This figure was set in charge of the keeping of five horses, strong and brave.

One night, late in autumn, long before the memory of the living, when the sound of drying leaves could be heard crunching beneath the feet of walkers and a damp heaviness moved in a stench upon the air, the Cóiste Bodhar set forth to take the soul of a kind and faithful man, who would be snuffed out in his prime by the bitter and vengeful works of his foes.

The horses, five strong proud cobs, knowing the loss to the world if such a soul were to be taken, rebelled and railed against their master's command. With a whip said to be made of spinal bones and feared for the power of its life-taking snap, he loomed above the horses to subdue them.

The fifth horse, the strongest horse, known by the name of Darp, hated the whip and grew wild and panicked at the thought of such a wrong. With a heavy hoof and relentless will, she broke the cords and chains that bound her to the coach and bolted into the wild fierceness of the unknown night.

And this is how Darp became one of the púcaí, the spirits of lore, mischief and, most of all, freedom, and she is said to often visit those lost and in need of a kind and caring friend.

Sometimes Darp appears as a terrifying horse of the night, huge and sleek, breathing thick, sooty blasts from her nostrils.

Her eyes are amber fire and her snort like thunder, and all about her lingers a smell of earthy turf and sulphur. To others she is the kind mare of the meadows.

Darp is said to linger on the edge, be it riversides or crossroads, at dusk, at dawn, at the turning of the seasons, as the first frosts touch the wild berries, at a birth, or at the spade's first turn of soil at the end of a life. Yet for all her frightful deeds, Darp, to the Mincéirí, was a tame creature, for like the Mincéirí, she too loved the freedom of the roads.

In the summer of 1920, during the sacking of Tuam, it is said that three young goklyns were separated from their family. They had wandered off in the morning to play and were unable to return home by the roads they had taken due to the commotion.

They knew they had to journey through the town to return to their family, but the streets were splashed with blood and filled with soot and ash from the burning of the buildings. Unfamiliar with the area and not knowing the safest roads to take, the three goklyns stood for a long time at the

edge of the town, on the rise of a small hill that overlooked many of the streets and buildings.

Not knowing whether to stay in case their family were on the way to find them or to return to the molly they had joyfully left that morning, the three children stood on the hill. A palpable fear screamed in the air around them and they began to weep, their limbs paralysed with fright.

Just before dusk began to fall and the cold blanket of night approached, the children heard a quick snort from behind them. They turned swiftly around and discovered a large cob, standing solid at the base of the hill, hooves half thrust into the soil. With a jolt of its head, it beckoned the children down to it. At first they did not move, for they did not know the horse, its temperament or who it belonged to, but again the horse snorted out a fresh breath and again it tossed its head to them in welcome.

One by one, with timid steps, the children moved down the hill to the horse. They found a calm creature who allowed them to pat her head and scratch beneath her chin. As soon as the last child had joined them, the horse began to steadily circle the three children, and with a gentle nudge of her head, pushed them forward towards the road.

Slowly the children obeyed and they started their journey through town. After a while the horse stopped circling the three children, knowing they trusted her. One took hold of her mane on the left, the second held her mane on the right, and the third and youngest child could only reach far enough to place his hand against her ribs as they walked, feeling both the strength of her hooves against the ground and the steady beating of her heart.

On the children followed the horse down laneways and byways, through the gaps between the gable ends of homes, through gardens and over cobble-locked pathways. At times they passed in front of gun-wielding soldiers and held their breaths. It was as if the mare and the three children were just like the winds, unseen along their journey.

At each branching of a road the horse would pause for a moment and again nudge the children in the direction they were to follow, and so this continued through the night until the three Mincéir children were within sight of their molly and worried family.

As soon as the children were in the embrace of their loved ones, they turned to show those in the camp the kind horse who had found them and guided them home to safety, but she was gone.

The horse had vanished, leaving only the kind markings of her presence in the minds of those she had met and the hoof prints in the grass through which she had safely led them home.

The well of lost wishes

A skrubol ara nil nok

One day, when driving on the road back from Dunmore, the lórk, which always thumped out plumes of ash and shuddered as it went, broke down.

I sat in the back seat flicking through the pages of a library book. Rebelliously, I made small comments in the margins in silver pencil. I told myself it would be okay as they could be easily scrubbed away using a scrunched-up heel of bread. All the while my sister, who has a much keener sense of direction than me and who wanted to return home sooner rather than later, sat in the front passenger seat voicing a strong opinion on which road to take.

Now, the car was unexpectedly tucked up at a high tilt on the kerb of the road. We found ourselves both miles from home and near an old well. The well was more or less rectangular in shape, and a small section of it was cut out where people used to enter, aided by a stump of a step. It was made from rows of limestone stacked neatly on top of each other. Thick veins of broad-leaf ivy stretched up along its side and reached across the top like interlacing fingers, as if to hold the well in place.

To calm the situation, my father began to tell us the story of that well, the well of lost wishes, and at the same time, he raised the bonnet of the lórk to see what he could mend.

One day a young Mincéir couple was walking along the way to the town of Dunmore. They were recently married and were still aglow with the warmth of freshly sparked love. Their journey was a kind one because of the fresh weather and their meandering on the road together. It was made all the more enjoyable by the exchange of lively discussion and witty thoughts.

The husband was bright-faced with sharp features. He had striking, chainy eyes, the colour of rain in a newly made blue-white tin vessel, and his long thin nose hooked downwards. He wore soft brown clothes over a starched white shirt, unusual garb for a man of his age. Stiff white clothing at that time was for those who did not have to toil, for the labours of the wider world were often messy and grimy.

His stern features would have made him look cruel if not for his air of friendliness, the light wisps of laughter lines beneath his eyes and across his brow, and the consistent curl of his smile, mostly hidden in the edges of his cheeks as if awaiting a humorous exchange.

She was taller than him, stronger in build, and was of a far more curious nature, more ready to listen, sooner to see and quicker to understand. Her eyes were the colour of freshly cracked chestnuts. She wore a dress of multiple layers in shades of deep malachite green with a burnt black around the edges. The shawl about her shoulders was crimson with splashes of cerise, the colour of squeezed raspberries, and a weave that held the tone of red summer wine.

She walked at a much slower pace than he, and her passage was always heralded by a light ticking sound upon the ground, made by her hawthorn kamog, which she used to support her pace and stride.

In her childhood years she had been struck by a rogue cart that had rolled down a steep hill, marking her knees, ankles and hips with such severity that, while she could still walk, she moved in a jarring, angular motion.

Although he was wide-footed and stumbled easily and she shuffled slowly, their individual paces somehow met in a soft chorus. He would lunge with wide steps to move forward and by the time he had gained a decent balance in his amble, she had always made her way up to meet him.

Along the journey to Dunmore, they came across a small well no more than twelve feet from the edge of the road. It was nestled between a thick tangle of brambles and the thorny growth and branches of a furze bush. The well itself was formed by rows of short rectangular stone blocks, stacked tightly on top of each other, until they took the shape of a three-by-four-foot rectangle, with tufts of grass bursting out at the lower outer edge. It had been crafted with such skill that only very few plants had woven their roots between the rare cracks and spaces between the blocks, with the passing of time.

As they passed the well together, the couple began to discuss wells, the legends surrounding them and the enduring tales of the wishes granted.

Stopping for a moment, the husband picked up a small round pebble, the size of an early autumn acorn, from the ground. He held it to his chest so that it could feel the beating of his heart and whispered into it a muttering of prayers. He approached the well and extending his arm, let the stone drop from his outstretched hand into the waiting waters.

The husband had made a wish.

To their surprise a loud gust of air rushed towards them. Like an unseen beast it shook the trees in its wake, rattled and threw aside the dry, crisp, fallen leaves and pulled sharply upon the clothes and even the very breath of the newlyweds.

Within a moment, as suddenly as it had started, the wind stilled into an eerie silence, only disturbed by the clattering of the twigs and branches that had been tossed aside, coming to their own stillness as they fell in light thuds to the ground.

The couple stood holding each other, arms entwined in a tight, protective embrace, in awe and fear of what had happened, until a gentle calmness drew over them. Once his fear was quenched, the husband spoke and told his wife how he had made a simple wish, not for himself, but for her and for whatever her heart truly desired.

She heard her husband, and with the kamog still lightly tucked beneath her arm, she took his hand, and with the direction of her gaze as a guide and the gentle rocking of her body, they danced.

They danced their first ever dance, the dance her heart had always desired, the dance that was never for her at the music of the Ballinasloe Fair, at meetings at the crossroads, at the céilís and the Friday evening gatherings. Even on her wedding day she had been denied the skips of joy and the swish and sway of music that caught her spirit.

There, beside the road, in a moment sacred to them, the young lovers danced.

Later that day they came upon a molly and told all that could understand of the wonders of the well – its gift, its blessing, its kind boon. The wife danced as she told of her gift and sang sweet songs loud into the air. The husband beaming with smiles at his wife's joy, swayed with her now and again. But mostly he left her to her delight, dancing the dance her heart wanted.

They told those of the molly that they were to arrive in Dunmore the next day but would be returning after the closing of the market and that they hoped that the well would be as kind to others as it was to them. As the new dawn broke, the couple danced and made their way to the selling place, and at the same time those of the molly gathered, spread the word of the gift and made foot towards the well.

And they went in droves – children were cured, sight was restored, animals long dry once again brought fresh milk, money was found to send to family in England, long lost family members somehow knew of each other's location, shelter was secured, safety was assured and all in the molly were happy.

That evening, just as the light rust of dusk was starting to scatter itself upon the sky, the young couple, taking the long way home, passed the well again.

This time, however, it was a far different sight.

The well, once open and with water to its brim, was now dry and stacked high with pebbles. The couple stood transfixed. They wondered what had happened and then solemnly made their way back to the molly.

On reaching the molly, they saw loudly weeping men, and women with their faces buried deep in their hands, their wild hair tangled between their fingers, and children who sat silently beside

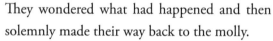

126

their parents knowing a great loss had taken place.

That morning, when word had travelled of the kind wish-granting well, a horde of people had gathered and journeyed to it, searching along the way for stones to toss.

At first the wishes were for things they held deep in their hearts, for health, for peace, for safety, but then they began to make frivolous wishes. The stones that were tossed towards the water held such light and empty intentions, it was like the careless throwing of pebbles into rain-filled puddles.

'Fix the hole in this pot', 'Let it not rain on Sunday', 'Find for me a pretty rose for my hair', 'Fill my pipe with tobacco', and on came the wishes as the well piled up with stones.

Sooner than expected, the well was full beyond its brim and people could make no more wishes.

After the filling of the well, many of the wishes started to undo, unravel and weaken. Within moments, the things wished for on whims began to fade away from sight and life.

Pretty dresses became grey and tattered, new carts showed the signs of rot, and prize-worthy mares began to pale and strain before the gaze of those who had willed them into being.

Those wishes that were not mere geigings but soulful callings for support, care and kindness were the only ones the well allowed to prevail.

Since that day when the wishing well was filled high with stones, the wells of Éire have rarely granted a wish. Every so often though, when the need is just, the want is real and the desire is for another, they listen, answer and gift a dance.

The screaming children

A lugil goklyns

Many of the older families in Ireland have tales of the fairies, the griwógs, the good people, the people of the mound and the gentry, that are passed from generation to generation. Travellers are among those who still share those tales, sometimes loudly and sometimes whispered around the fire, teacups raised in the company of friends.

They are tales of fright or fortune, of being silently taken or abruptly returned, of losses lamented or lovers lured, of gifts and curses, and so many adventures. For many Travellers, however, the griwógs are not creatures that live 'out there', for some of us, too, live 'out there'. They live in our midst, undetected.

My grandmother had many stories of the griwógs that she would tell to us to enchant the nights and leave us drawing our blankets high above our heads at bedtime to make sure that we wouldn't accidentally see something that might just see us too.

She would tell us never to throw out water in the night, to beware of quick-twisting leaves in the wind, not to follow gaps in the grass or bush line when out walking, unless it was an old path made by people known, and never to climb Knockma Hill alone.

Her wise words and bright insights instilled in us all the urge to listen, reflect and to try to truly hear the stories of the griwógs.

For a few months when I was in my early twenties, my grandmother lived with me on and off. My own mother would stay, too, to guide, mind and oversee. We squeezed into my small patch of a house which consisted of one bedroom, a nook of a bathroom and a kitchen and living room divided only by a white and black Stanley range.

Both claimed my bedroom without any protest from me and I slept in the softness of the sitting room sofa, propped up high by the vast collection of random pillows and cushions purchased from the local second-hand shops, my own little addiction.

They stayed most nights during that time, especially those nights when my grandmother had returned from a hospital visit or was touched by an unexpected tiredness and wanted people about her.

One evening, unexpectedly, as we sat together in my living room, came the comment from my grandmother: 'I know what I saw, heard and felt. It happened.'

I knew immediately what she was speaking of and I wondered what had taken place to bring the story to her mind. I had heard it, of course, indeed we all had, from my mother and from others. It had become a well-worn and often visited family tale, told with complete acceptance and shared with no sense of embarrassment or scepticism, but I had never heard it from my grandmother herself, who kept such things close to her heart like well-polished rubies.

I sat with her and listened, drinking milky too-sweet tea, just the way she liked it, poured from a light-blue earthenware teapot.

Teresa was young, about nine, a tall, thin girl in a brown dress, when she wandered down from the family camp, trading eggs from a wicker basket, the handle of which had failed in age and had been replaced with a long slip of blue cloth that rested on her shoulder. She visited the local households, gaining farthings and small bundles of turf, messages of family, and even a candle or two.

As the evening drew in, a light cold drizzle began to fall, and Teresa decided to return home. Along the way she saw a group of children, about ten in total, scattered across a field like marbles thrown into a wide bramble. Each was wearing a brightly coloured shirt, morning yellow, fresh crimson and mossy green, and long brown pants that were wide enough at the end to cover their feet and loose enough at the waist that the excess material hung over so neither belt nor tie could be seen.

Teresa continued along her path, keeping a keen eye on the children. She saw as she drew closer that they were playing kick with a ball that looked like a bundle of ragged old clothes tied tightly with many strings into a rough oval shape. She noticed that the ball often fell into a well near the centre of the field.

As she moved closer, her eyes widened when she realised that the children jumped in and out of the well to get the ball without effort and stayed dry. Confused at the sight, she came to a stop on the edge of the grassland and observed them as they played.

After a few moments the children realised that they were being watched and suddenly stilled and turned towards her as if controlled by one mind, each head twisting at the same speed and angle in an unnatural grinding motion.

For the first time, she got a full view of their still faces. Unlike the youth she expected to see, they were old, worn and wrinkled, their skin waxy and cracked like old apples left out in rough winter weather or blistering sun. Their eyes were yellow, the colour of spoiled egg yolks.

They screamed in unison, a chorus of shrill voices that cut through her. Startled, Teresa dropped her basket. Their cry was like nails on stone, a knife on a plate and the high hum of bees. They stood with their mouths gaping ever wider, as if their jaws had been unlocked and dropped down so their chins rested on the middle of their chests. The drawn-out sound shook the very core of her young bones. She felt as if she was caught on a rickety cart, shaking and swaying on a pothole-filled road. The sound continued, etched ever deeper into her temples, piercing like a finely smithed pin against flesh.

She took flight. With her instincts as her guide, she found herself sprinting in the direction of her family and safety.

As she took a sharp left, they followed. She raced through puddles and bushes as they chased her. She could feel fingertips graze the back of her plaits, sometimes getting close enough to make her jolt her head forwards. She whipped her head from side to side so that the fingers could not become fists in her mane. Small, stubby hands grasped at her dress, catching it now and again as she turned. She snapped her dress forward out of their reach. When this failed to remove them, she reached down, not caring for finger nor nail, and dug her hands into the cold flesh of the children's fingers, until, like the bite of dogs, their hold was released.

She moved like a hare, darting, dashing, covering the ground as fast as her will and body would allow her.

Eventually she came to the corner of her home, crying loudly, her words more like the dry tone of carrion crows than speech, and nearly without breath. In exhaustion, her knees gave way as soon as she heard her mother's sweet welcome.

With mud on nearly every inch of her dress and panic weighing on her, she told her mother and her father what had happened. At first she expected a scolding for losing the wicker basket and its contents but instead, to her great relief, her father kissed the top of her head in blessing and her mother wrapped her arms tightly around her, and as soon as she had let go of the embrace the family quickly started to pack up and move.

Teresa paced the grass alongside the cart. It took her several hours to return to a sense of peace. She waited for the wheels of the cart to turn, hoping that they would soon be on their way and out of sight of the old camp.

With their home and everything they owned stacked high behind them on the cart, they took the road that cut across the playing field where she had seen the griwógs. Her mother had her legs over the edge of the cart, while Teresa wrapped hers up against her chest, her arms crossed about them as tight as an early autumn acorn. She was tucked snugly under her mother's black and tawny-brown shawl, nestled against her chest with the fabric pressed against her face, leaving only her eyes exposed to catch glimpses of the field. Her mother ran her fingers though her hair as they sat on the back of the horse-drawn cart, keeping her close and whispering soft-toned blessings now and again to assure her of her safety.

She was never again followed in that way, but the experience carved a deep mark into my grandmother's life, a cry that echoed so strongly that her grandchildren, too, heard it. We never knew if the tale was true or not, but it was real enough to our grandmother, and that was more than enough for us.

The dance of smoke and midges

A Féin an a clags

Each time I have heard this story, the teller has brought and lost elements. It has stretched and shrunk more times than the tides on the sandy beaches of memory. Stories are how we explain the world around us to others and ourselves. It is a way to find mirrors and roadmaps, sense and silliness, as well as to fill evenings and mornings and all the hours between with adventures and connections. Each story passes messages to us, some clear, some oblique, but always speaking to us when we choose to listen.

From an early age, I knew that stories were told with the understanding that they would be retold. They carry the past and present of the teller in them, together reweaving an ancient tapestry.

It was in Leenaun, County Galway, on the Killary fjord, at the foot of Mweelrea that I first heard this story as we sat around a small campfire stacked low but wide, no higher than your ankle and the breadth of an arm. It was beside the river where my great-grandparents and grandparents used to stop that my parents, my aunt and uncle and all of us children camped that day. It was in the height of summer and we had spent many hours rolling down the grassy hill and searching the river for pyrite, the fool's gold. Several chunks were found and young wild dreams were spun with the fancy of it being real.

The air was high in midges and we children, lazing by the fire, kept moving left and right every few minutes with the wind as it shifted the smoke gently from the small blaze. There was a trick to it – stay near enough to the smoke-filled breeze as it passed by to keep the midges from you, but not close enough to the gust that it would blow right onto you.

It was easy at first, that dance of smoke and midges, but after a while it grew annoying having to move, to flick them away in the air, to scratch. We were instructed to pick the dried rushes by the riverside, brown from age and the fully risen sun. We took them in small bundles of six or eight to the fire, using them like little incense sticks to wave in the air, drifting silver shields to keep the midges away.

'Do you know where they come from,' asked the stoker of the fire, 'the midges?'

'No,' we said, and so we were told.

There was once a man, at least it was the shape of a man, known only as the Féin. He was tall and strong and had eyes the colour of the bright moss that grows on the branches of the ash tree. His voice moved with a melody unlike any other. His laughter was said to be rich and rose like bubbling spring air through gentle moving brooks, and he had a walk that was smooth with steps as light as a falling feather. He wore a small sackcloth bag that rested tightly on his hip.

His heart, however, his heart was another thing.

The Féin was known to arrive at camps to a welcome. People trusted him, gathered around him and listened to his tales, won over by his enchanting presence and the sense of cheer he brought with him.

The Féin stayed one, two, three nights at most at any camp. His days were spent helping the men in whatever work they were undertaking, be it the stripping of copper, the keeping of the horses, the making of blackthorn walking sticks, the mending of pots, or the making of pans. He would do all but stack the fire, neither tending to flame, removing the soot nor gathering kindling wood.

In the evening he would spin his tales, amuse people with songs and often present those assembled with a bottle of honey ale.

All was well when the Féin visited. At first. However, he brought something with him, unseen, but heavily felt once he left. It was here in Leenaun, at an old camp, that things came to be seen as they truly were.

It was autumn when the family rested there. The work on the land was finished and the darker, dim days were slowly drawing in. When the candles and lamp oil became all the more precious, when resting spaces, sheltering places, winter havens were being discussed, that was when the Féin visited.

At first it was wonderful, hearing fresh tales, new songs, word of family far away, but soon, sooner than expected, came the turning of it all.

People went to bed with a calm warmth in their hearts and awoke, earlier than usual, with dryness in their throats, soreness in their heads, cramps in their stomachs and a looseness in their gums.

It was worse for the young, the goklyns. When the Féin came, he brought fun and joy, and when he left, he took them with him. Age came over people like a slow-moving sheet, draped by a concealed hand. From those already aged he took little, but from the young he took a lot. Bright eyes became sullen, clear skin became grey, and teeth, even those new and fresh as little pearls, dropped out.

Usually families would crush-auin out of the place as soon as the sickness came, thinking that the land had soured against them. Few would think of the Féin.

This time a child no taller than my hip had turned in a sickness. The mother boiled herbs and teas for her and the father took to the road in search of a doctor. Night came swiftly and claimed the camp.

The mother heard a rustle from the widdle tent and, expecting the father to have returned with some cure or bottle for her child, rose to meet him. She looked around until she saw an unfamiliar shape by the fire. It was not the cut of her husband. On a closer look she realised it was the Féin, who looked fresher in appearance than when he had departed and was glancing at the ground around him.

'Féin! You frightened me! What are you doing here?' said the mother as she looked at the Féin, whose body was rigid and angular, shifting in sharp, rough motions, very unlike how he had been known.

'The teeth,' he replied in a voice as sharp and cold as wrought iron.

'What?' said the mother in reply, stepping slightly back towards the tent in her confusion and growing concern.

'The teeth,' said the Féin again, his eyes boring into her. 'I've come for the teeth,' he said, more sharply this time, with a curl of menace in his voice, raising the roughly woven sackcloth bag. 'I've come and fed you all very well, now I'll eat what is mine to take!'

The mother, glancing fearfully at the tent in which her children slept, moved forward in strength against his words. 'Move along now, Féin, move along. We want no more of this!' she cried out.

'Not until I've taken what is mine!' shouted the Féin as he lunged towards the tent, towards the children, towards their fallen teeth.

'Not mine!' screamed the mother, pushing him back with her work-strong hands.

The Féin, barely moved by her efforts, looked over her and stepped closer to the sleeping children.

Breaths rapid, body clenched in panic, the mother moved swiftly in front of the cruel, darksome figure lurching towards her children's tent. In desperation, she thrust her full weight against the twisted figure.

The grass was wet that chilly evening with late-season dew. The push became a swivel for the Féin, who turned unexpectedly and stumbled back, not anticipating the force.

He fell and landed on the flames of the campfire and, like a match, he was aflame. It was not a lingering flame, not a dull one, but a quick one, like fresh parchment paper set ablaze.

Within seconds he was gone. No longer was he the shape of a man, the guise of a friend, the cut of the Féin, but just a pile of grey ash.

The mother fell back on the ground, clutching at the grass as she tumbled to stop herself toppling over. She sat there for moments, her breath quick and not quite understanding what had happened. On gathering her senses, she made for the tent of her sleeping children and saw that their breathing had softened and the colours of life had returned to their once again youthful faces.

Her husband returned to the camp and, noticing immediately the disorder, approached his wife in near panic. She calmed him. All was indeed well, the children safe, herself sound, and the Féin unexpectedly taken by the flames.

Soon enough the dawn was peeking through on the horizon. The father, unsetting the camp for a move, was deeply bothered by what had happened and gathered up the fire and Féin ash and brought it to the riverside. Before he could throw it to the ripples, to the wild water to be carried away, the wind took the ash in a sudden gust.

The windswept ash rose high and formed a swarming flurry of darting black flies, that in a single motion took the figure of the Féin. Then, within a moment, the midges scattered taking with them the last sight of that otherworldly creature.

This was the birth of the first midges, creatures that fester and feed on human skin, clinging on and biting when they can. They were born from a hunger to feast, made ravenous by the flavour of youth and agitated by the energy of their meal.

Midges still linger, especially in summer and autumn, bothering, troubling, disturbing.

No one quite knows where he came from, no one quite knows where he went, but even now it's best to bury the fallen teeth than welcome the Féin to your home.

We shuffled into the tent, eyes and ears alert to any midges that might be about and we gave an extra sweep to our teeth in the morning. Still now, years later, we whisper to rebellious children, 'Quick, be quiet, the Féin might take you!'